21ST CENTURY ROCK

WISE PUBLICATIONS
LONDON / NEW YORK / PARIS / SYDNEY / COPENHAGEN / BERLIN / MADRID / TOKYO

EXCLUSIVE DISTRIBUTORS:
MUSIC SALES LIMITED
8/9 FRITH STREET, LONDON W1D 3JB,
ENGLAND.
MUSIC SALES PTY LIMITED
120 ROTHSCHILD AVENUE, ROSEBERY,
NSW 2018, AUSTRALIA.

ORDER NO. AM976866
ISBN 0-7119-9880-9
THIS BOOK © COPYRIGHT 2003
BY WISE PUBLICATIONS.

COMPILED BY NICK CRISPIN.
MUSIC ARRANGED BY JAMES DEAN.
MUSIC PROCESSED BY ANDREW SHIELS.

COVER DESIGN BY FRESH LEMON.
PRINTED IN MALTA BY
INTERPRINT LIMITED.

YOUR GUARANTEE OF QUALITY:
AS PUBLISHERS, WE STRIVE TO PRODUCE EVERY
BOOK TO THE HIGHEST COMMERCIAL STANDARDS.
THE MUSIC HAS BEEN FRESHLY ENGRAVED AND
THE BOOK HAS BEEN CAREFULLY DESIGNED
TO MINIMISE AWKWARD PAGE TURNS AND TO
MAKE PLAYING FROM IT A REAL PLEASURE.
PARTICULAR CARE HAS BEEN GIVEN TO
SPECIFYING ACID-FREE, NEUTRAL-SIZED
PAPER MADE FROM PULPS WHICH HAVE
NOT BEEN ELEMENTAL CHLORINE BLEACHED.
THIS PULP IS FROM FARMED SUSTAINABLE
FORESTS AND WAS PRODUCED WITH
SPECIAL REGARD FOR THE ENVIRONMENT.
THROUGHOUT, THE PRINTING AND BINDING HAVE
BEEN PLANNED TO ENSURE A STURDY,
ATTRACTIVE PUBLICATION WHICH
SHOULD GIVE YEARS OF ENJOYMENT.
IF YOUR COPY FAILS TO MEET OUR HIGH STANDARDS,
PLEASE INFORM US AND WE WILL GLADLY REPLACE IT.

WWW.MUSICSALES.COM

GUITAR TABLATURE EXPLAINED

Guitar music can be notated three different ways: on a musical stave, in tablature, and in rhythm slashes

RHYTHM SLASHES are written above the stave. Strum chords in the rhythm indicated. Round noteheads indicate single notes.

THE MUSICAL STAVE shows pitches and rhythms and is divided by lines into bars. Pitches are named after the first seven letters of the alphabet.

TABLATURE graphically represents the guitar fingerboard. Each horizontal line represents a string, and each number represents a fret.

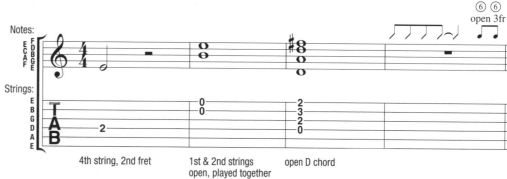

4th string, 2nd fret

1st & 2nd strings open, played together

open D chord

DEFINITIONS FOR SPECIAL GUITAR NOTATION

SEMI-TONE BEND: Strike the note and bend up a semi-tone (1/2 step).

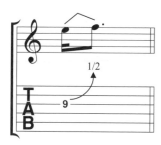

WHOLE-TONE BEND: Strike the note and bend up a whole-tone (whole step).

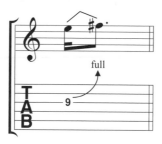

GRACE NOTE BEND: Strike the note and bend as indicated. Play the first note as quickly as possible.

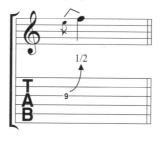

QUARTER-TONE BEND: Strike the note and bend up a 1/4 step.

BEND & RELEASE: Strike the note and bend up as indicated, then release back to the original note.

COMPOUND BEND & RELEASE: Strike the note and bend up and down in the rhythm indicated.

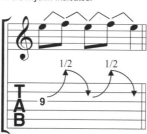

PRE-BEND: Bend the note as indicated, then strike it.

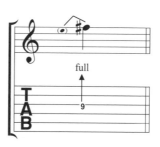

PRE-BEND & RELEASE: Bend the note as indicated. Strike it and release the note back to the original pitch.

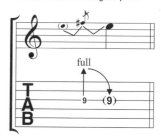

HAMMER-ON: Strike the first note with one finger, then sound the second note (on the same string) with another finger by fretting it without picking.

PULL-OFF: Place both fingers on the notes to be sounded, strike the first note and without picking, pull the finger off to sound the second note.

LEGATO SLIDE (GLISS): Strike the first note and then slide the same fret-hand finger up or down to the second note. The second note is not struck.

MUFFLED STRINGS: A percussive sound is produced by laying the fret hand across the string(s) without depressing, and striking them with the pick hand.

NATURAL HARMONIC: Strike the note while the fret-hand lightly touches the string directly over the fret indicated.

PICK SCRAPE: The edge of the pick is rubbed down (or up) the string, producing a scratchy sound.

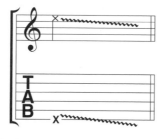

PALM MUTING: The note is partially muted by the pick hand lightly touching the string(s) just before the bridge.

SHIFT SLIDE (GLISS & RESTRIKE): Same as legato slide, except the second note is struck.

NOTE: The speed of any bend is indicated by the music notation and tempo.

ALL MY LIFE

WORDS & MUSIC BY DAVE GROHL, NATE MENDEL, TAYLOR HAWKINS & CHRIS SHIFLETT

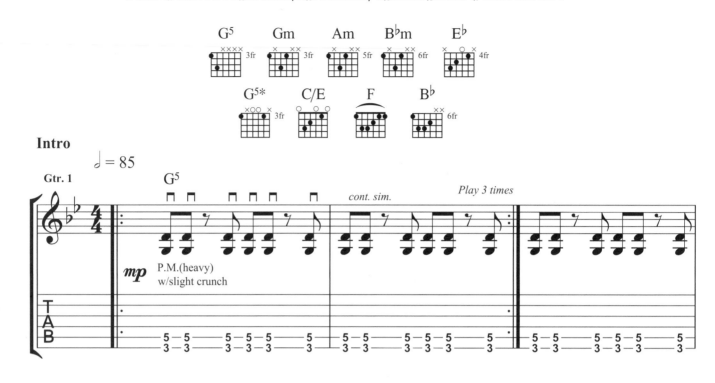

All my life I've been search-ing for some-thing__ some - thing ne-ver comes ne - ver

leads to no - thing,__ no - thing sa-tis-fies but I'm gett-ing__ close,__ clos-

- er to the prize__ at the end of the rope.__ All night long I dream__

__ of the day, when__ it comes a - round then it's ta - ken a - way,__ leaves__

__ me with the feel - ing that I feel the__ most,__ feel - ing comes to life__ when I

see your__ ghost__

Gm   Am

Gtrs. 1+2*

sfz w/dist.
P.M. off

cont. sim.

* composite part: Gtr. 1 plays 6th string only
Gtr. 2 plays upper part

5

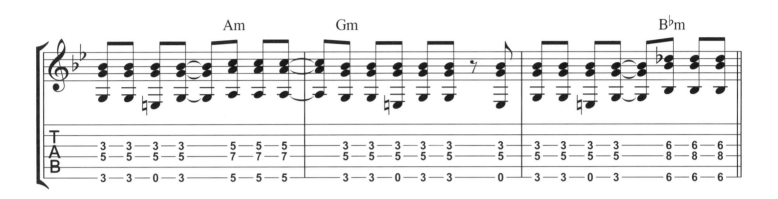

Verse

1. Come down don't you re - sist you've such a de - li - cate wrist
2. Will I find a be - liev - er a - no - ther one who be - lieves?

Gtrs. 1+2*

*Composite part

_____ and if I give it a twist_____
_____ A - no - ther one to de - ceive_____

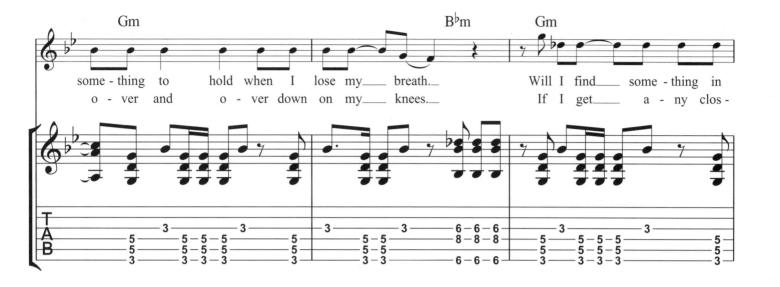

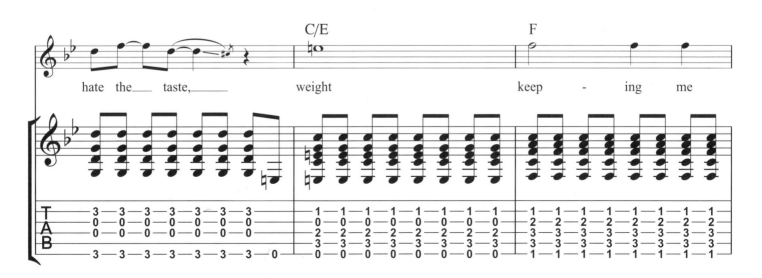

8

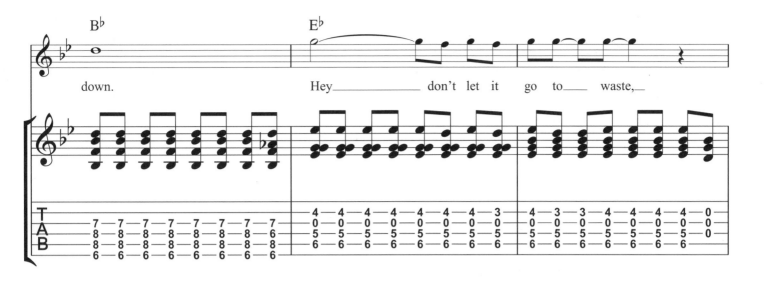

down.

Hey_____ don't let it go to___ waste,___

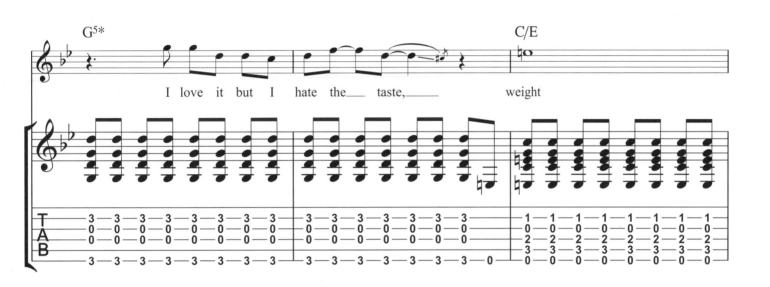

I love it but I hate the___ taste,_____ weight

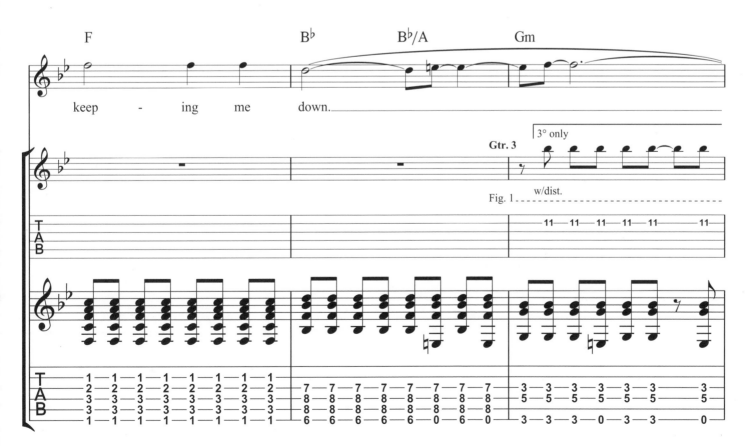

keep - ing me down._____

Gtr. 3

3° only

Fig. 1 -
w/dist.

Am   Gm   B♭m

G⁵

Gtr. 2   *cont. sim.*

Vocal tacet 1°

Gtr. 1

All   my   life   I've   been   search - ing   for   some -   thing____   some -

(Tacet 1°)

mp P.M.(heavy)
w/slight crunch

- thing   ne - ver   comes   ne - ver   leads   to   no - thing,____   no -   thing   sa - tis - fies   but   I'm

Another Morning Stoner

Words & Music by Kevin Allen, Neil Busch, Conrad Keely & Jason Reece

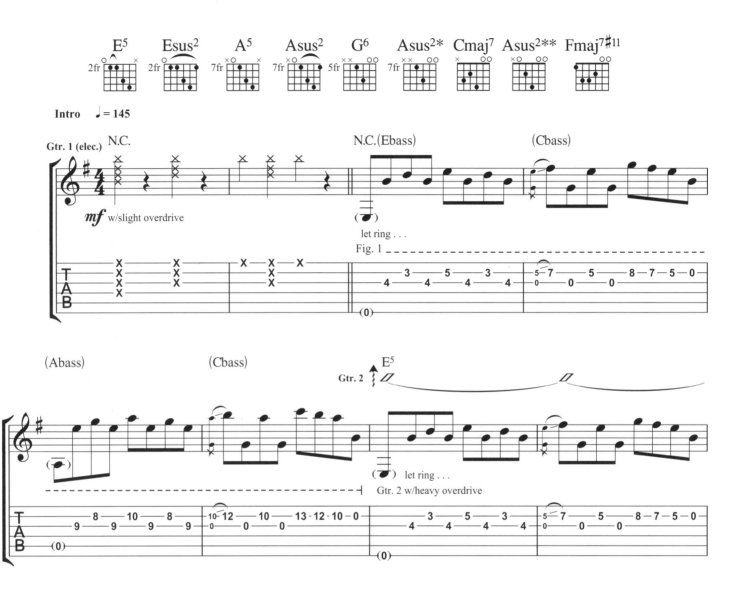

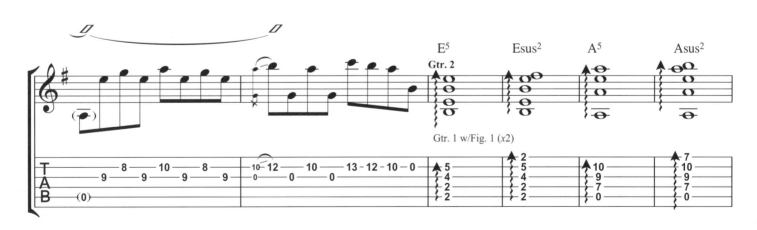

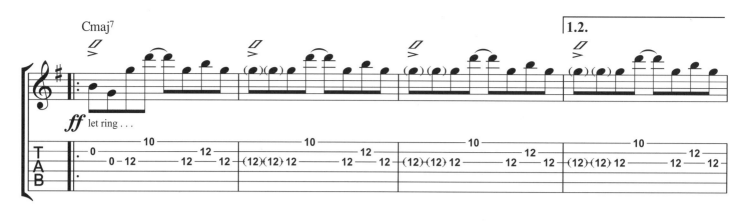

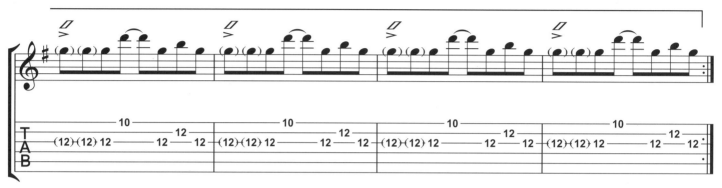

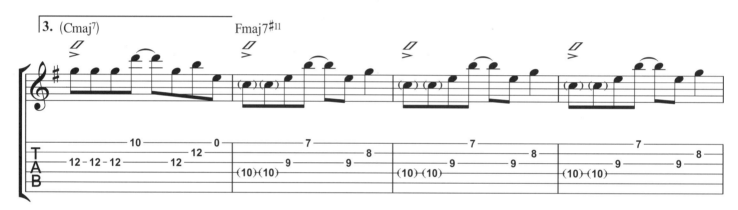

CRAWLING

WORDS & MUSIC BY CHESTER BENNINGTON, ROB BOURDON, BRAD DELSON, JOSEPH HAHN & MIKE SHINODA

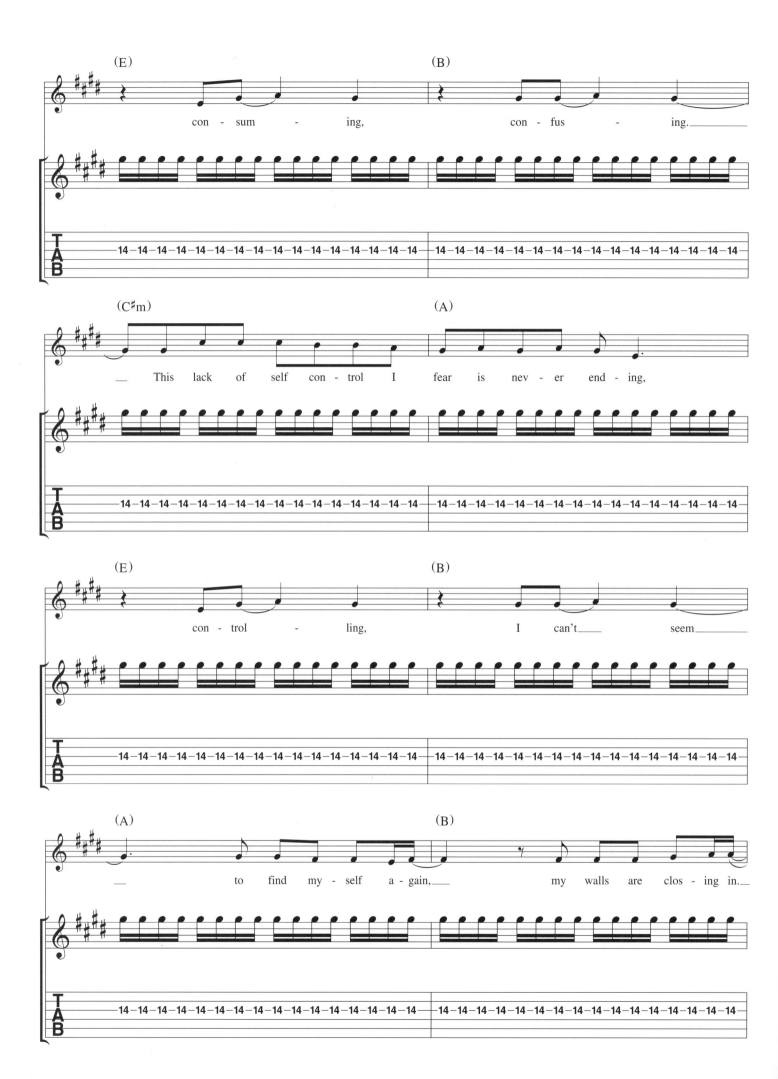

(C♯m)

(Without a sense of confidence, I'm convinced that there's just too much pressure to take.)

(A)   (B)

I've felt this way be - fore,___ so in - se -

(C♯m)

- cure.___

ff w/distortion

Chorus
C♯5   A5   C♯5   B5   G♯5

Crawl - ing in my skin, these wounds they will not he - al,___

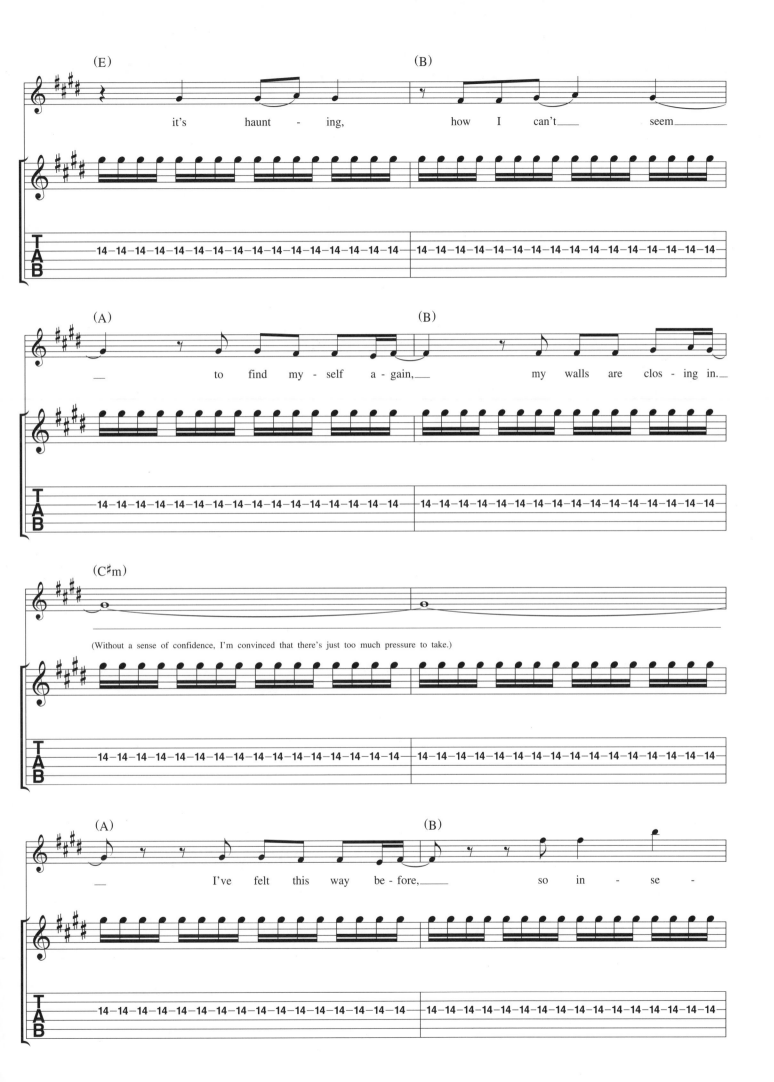

CHOP SUEY!
WORDS BY SERJ TANKIAN & DARON MALAKIAN
MUSIC BY DARON MALAKIAN

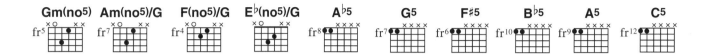

Tune gtr. Drop D tuning, down a tone:

⑥ = C   ③ = F
⑤ = G   ② = A
④ = C   ① = D

* chords in brackets refer to standard tuning chord shapes/positions

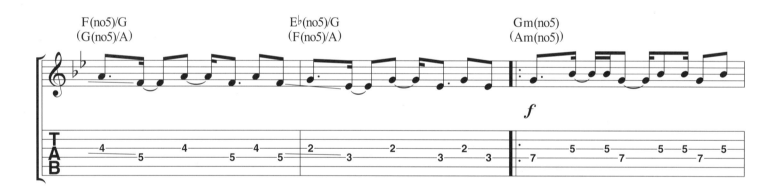

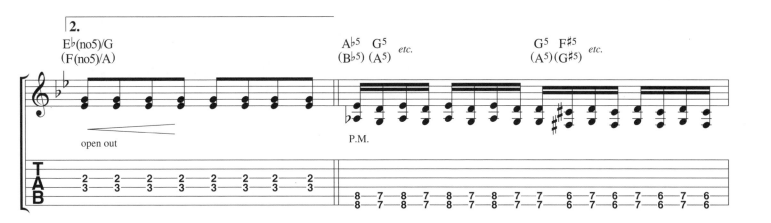

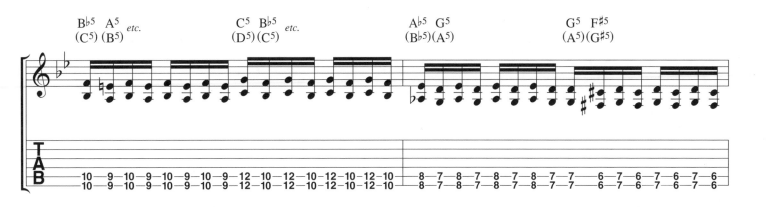

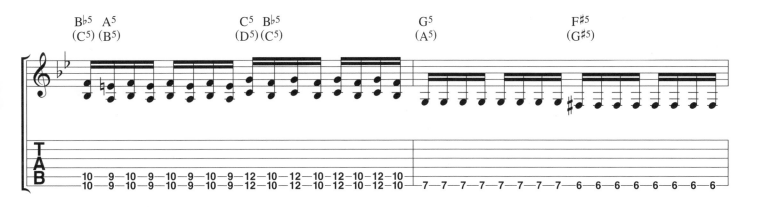

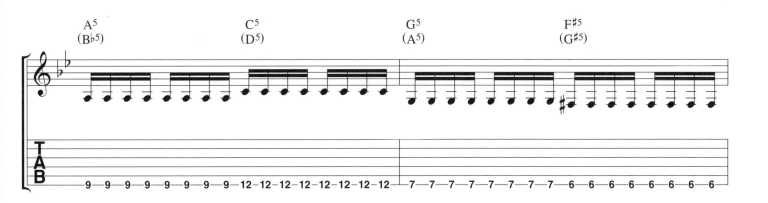

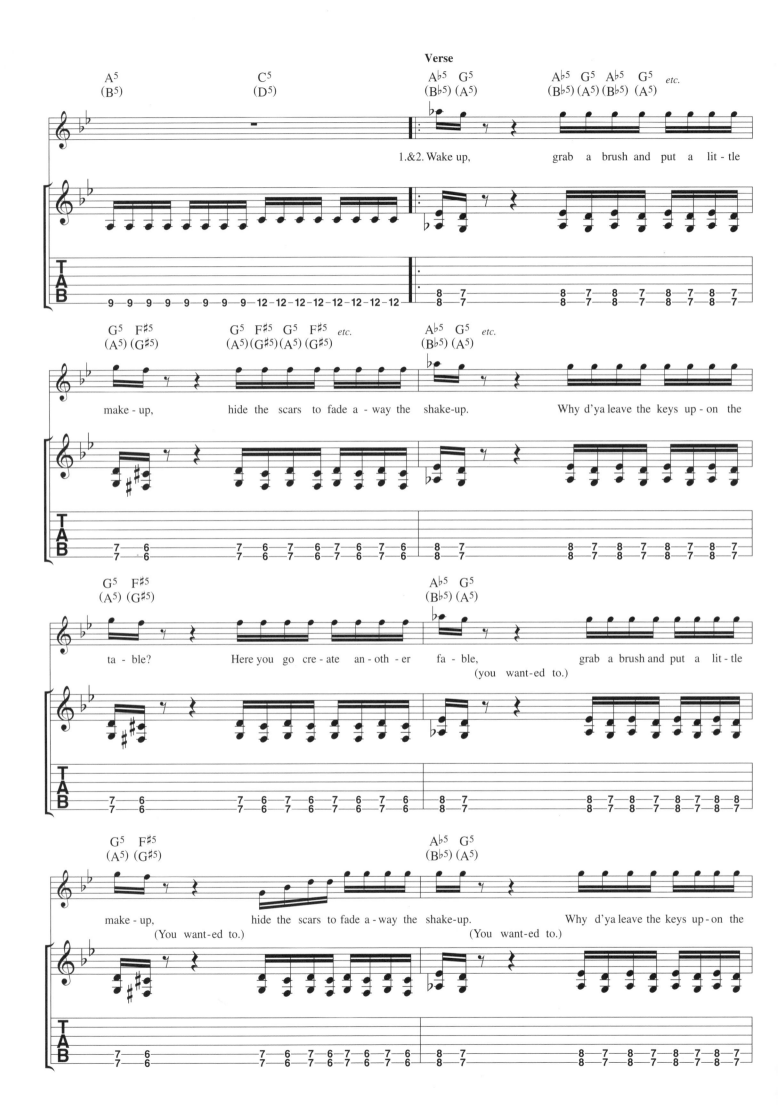

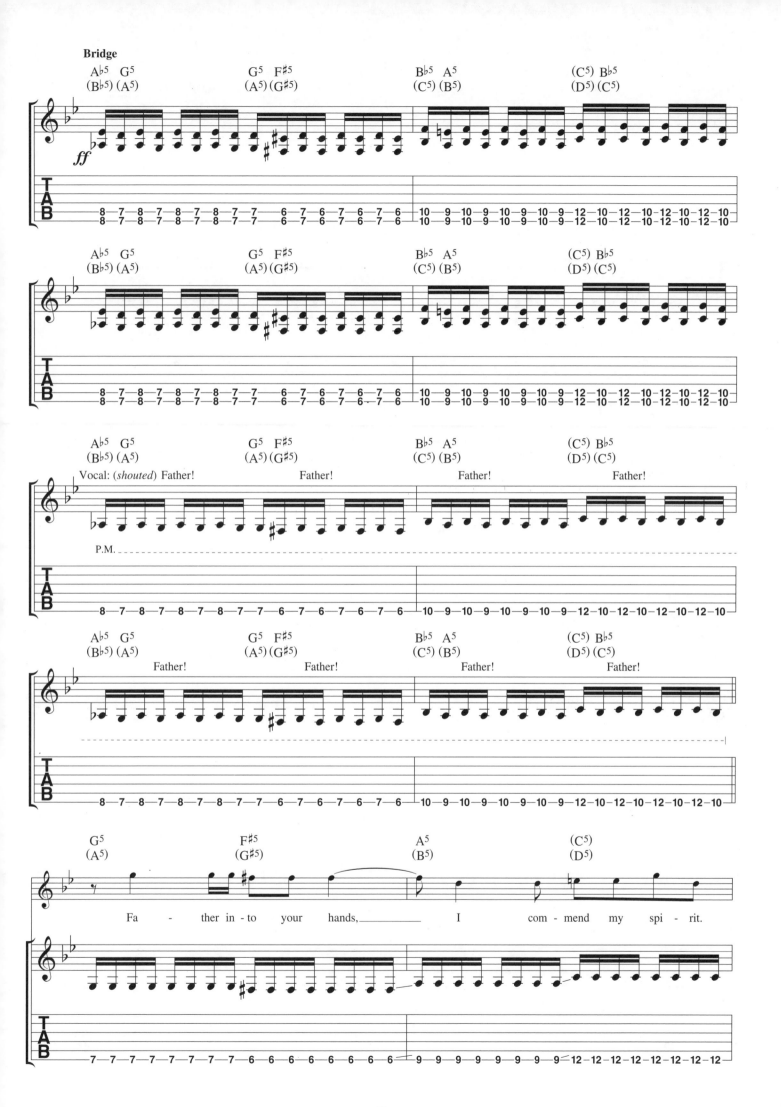

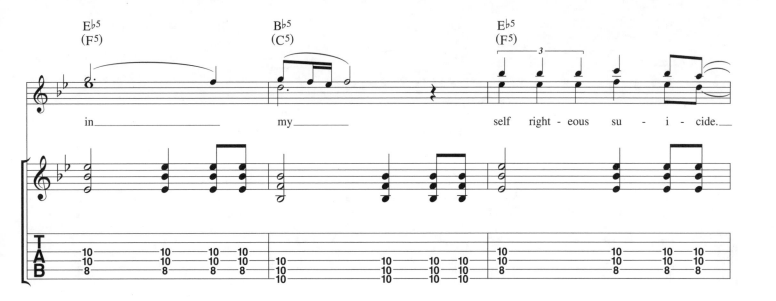

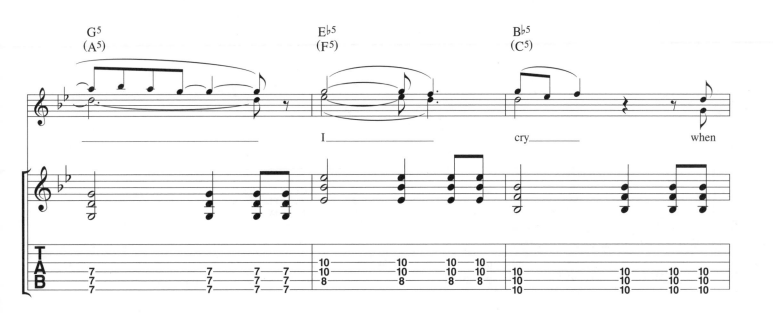

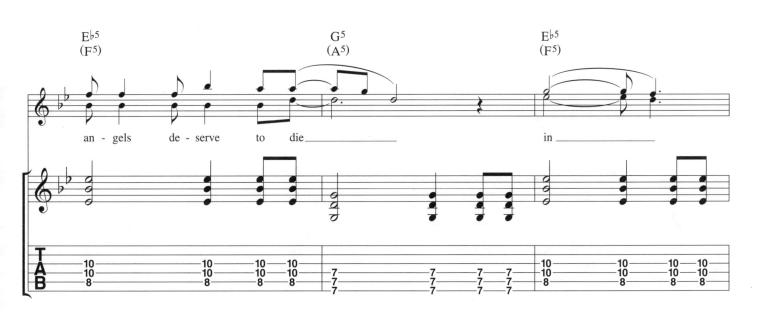

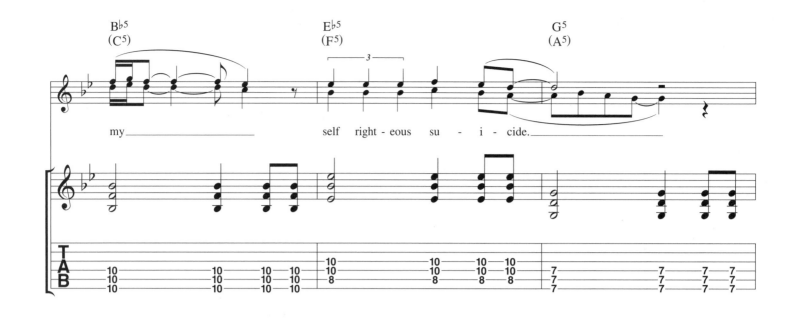

my_____ self right - eous su - i - cide.

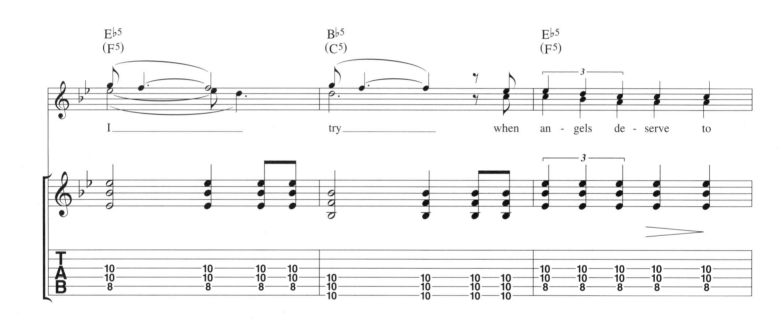

I_____ try_____ when an - gels de - serve to

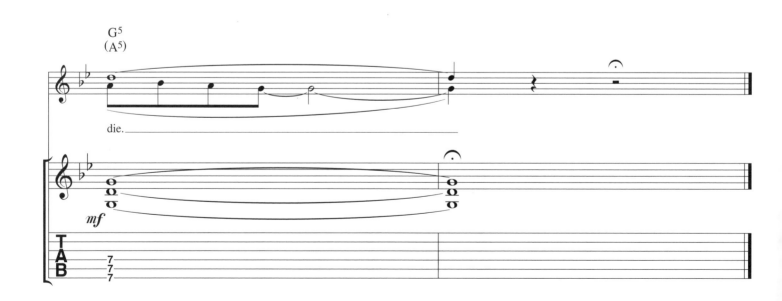

die._____

DEAD STAR

LYRICS & MUSIC BY MATTHEW BELLAMY

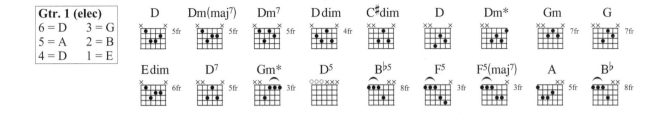

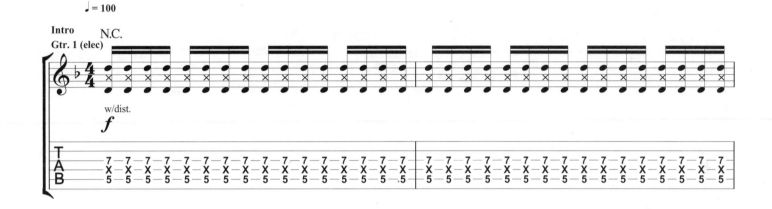

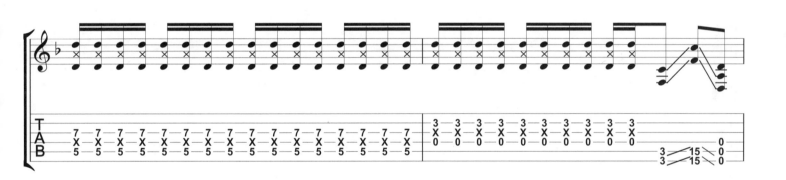

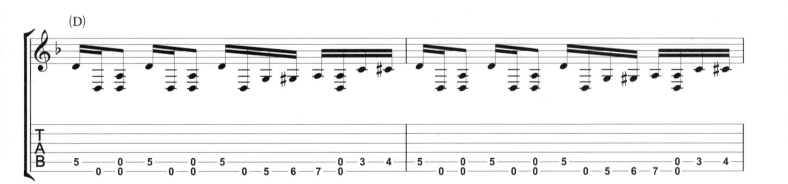

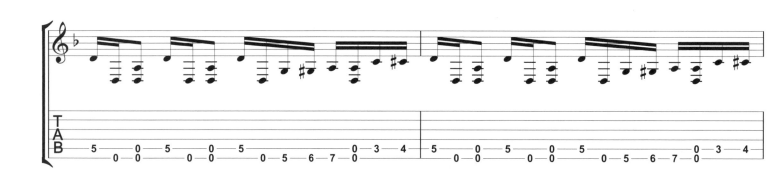

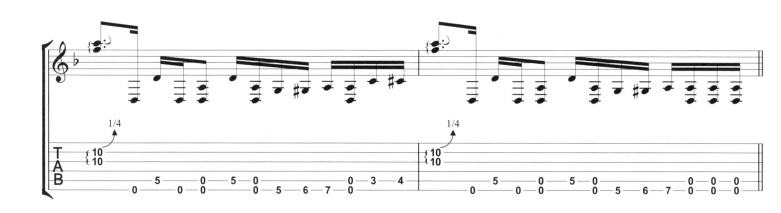

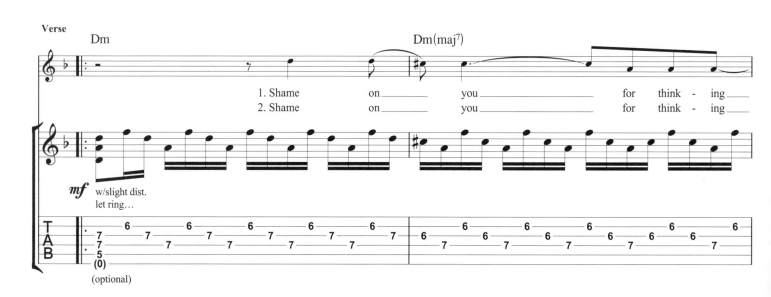

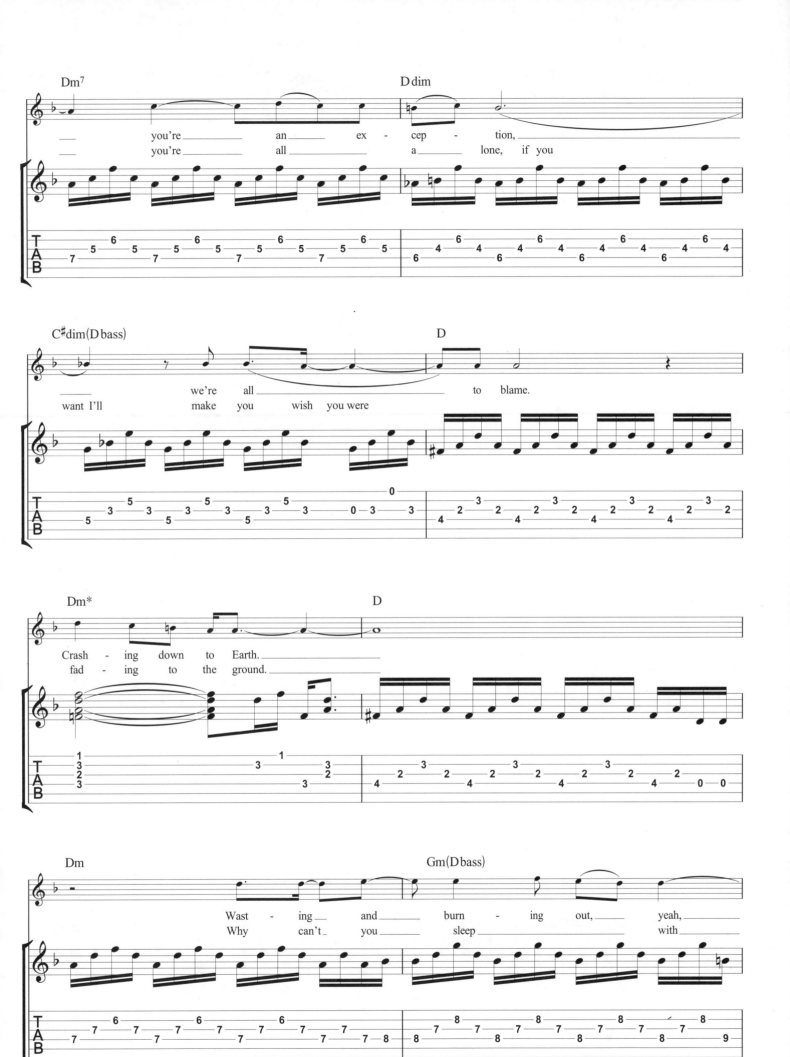

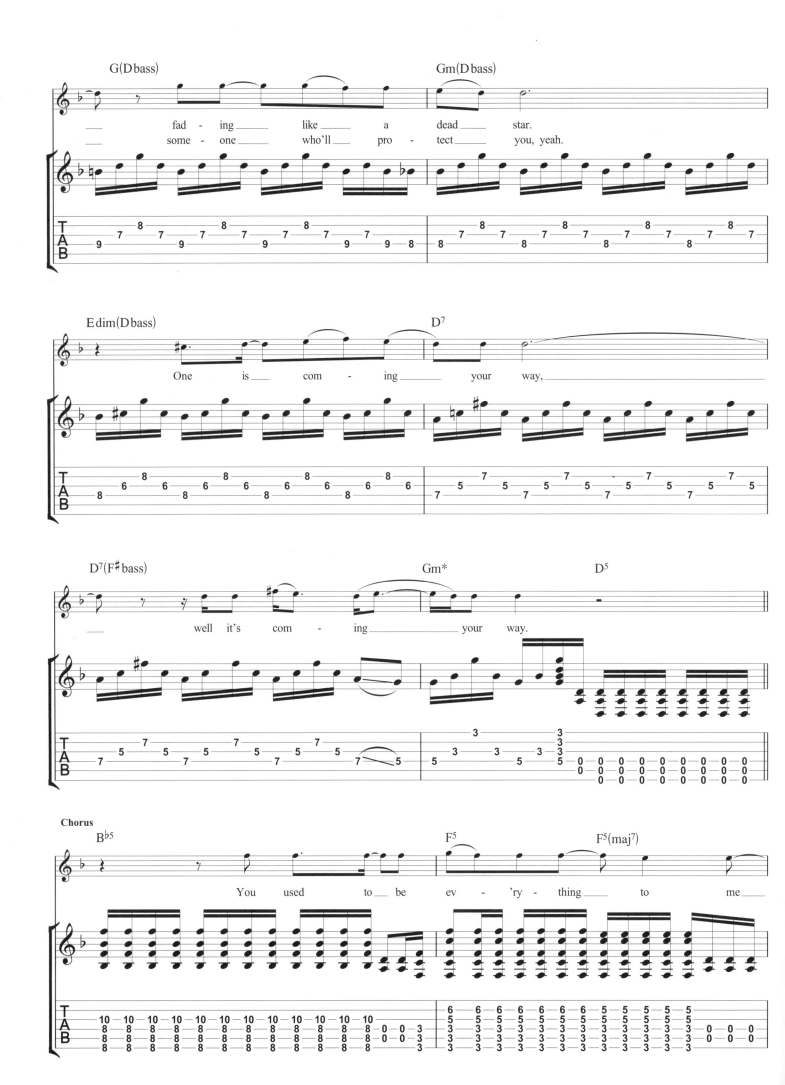

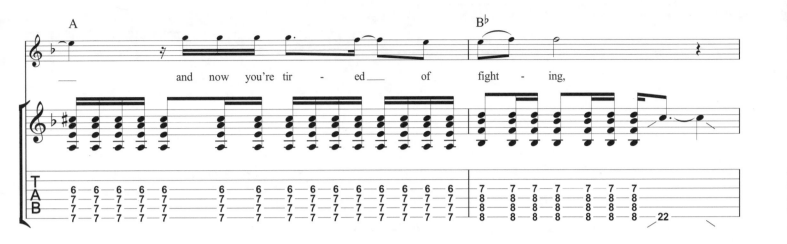

and now you're tir - ed___ of fight - ing,

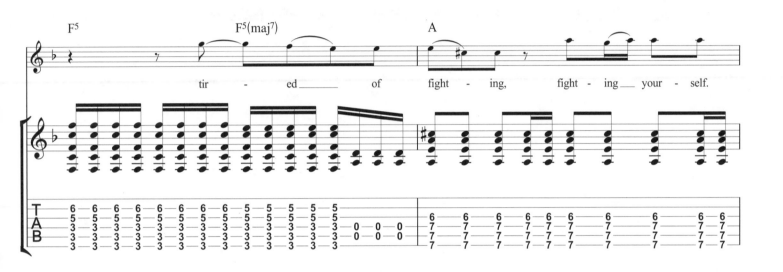

tir - ed___ of fight - ing, fight - ing___ your - self.

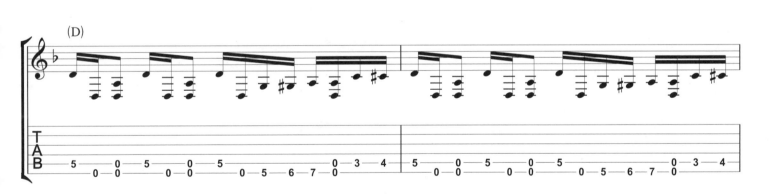

41

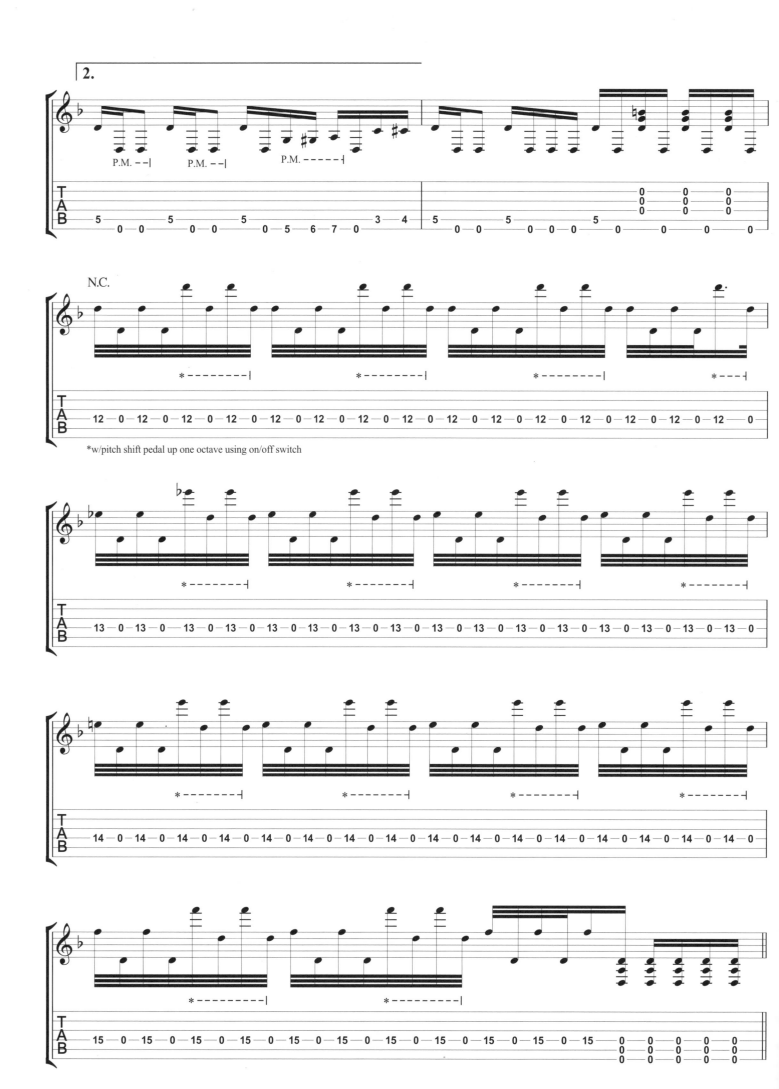

*w/pitch shift pedal up one octave using on/off switch

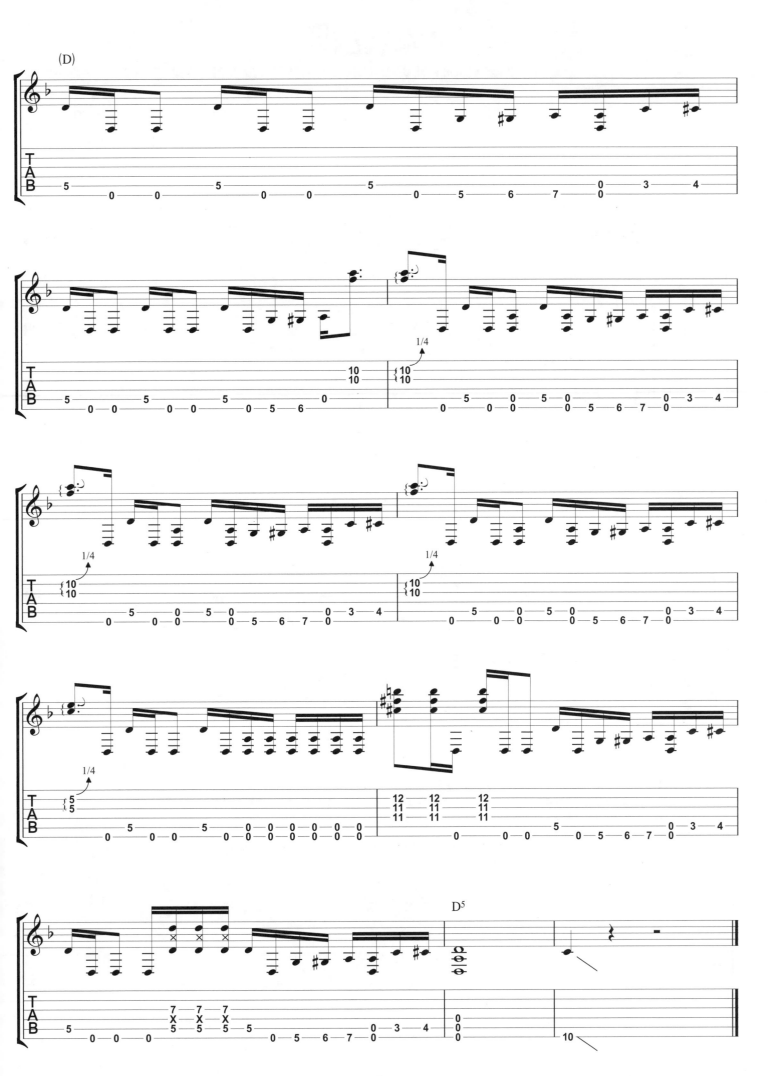

FAT LIP

WORDS & MUSIC BY GREIG NORI, DERYCK WHIBLEY, STEVE JOCZ & DAVE BAKSH

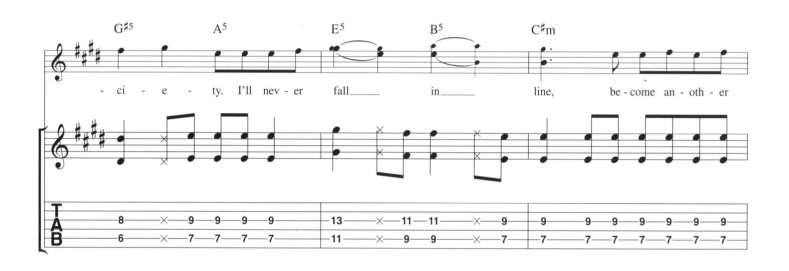

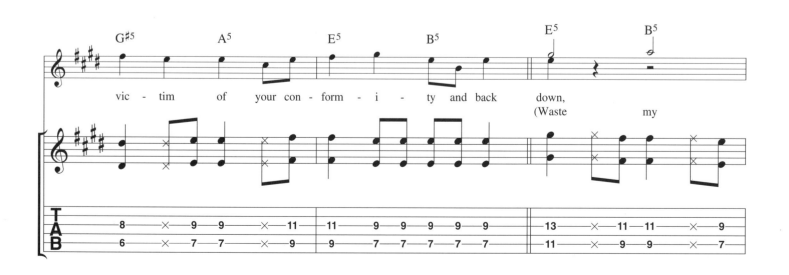

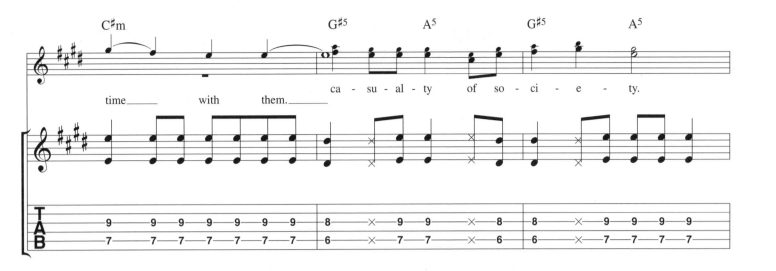

ca - su - al - ty of so - ci - e - ty.

time___ with them.___

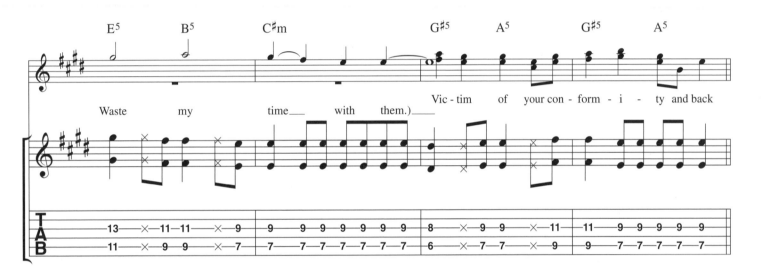

Waste my time___ with them.)___

Vic - tim of your con - form - i - ty and back

Outro
Half tempo ($\flat$ = $\flat$)

down.

* w/echo repeats

FEEL GOOD HIT OF THE SUMMER

Words & Music by Joshua Homme & Nick Oliveri

Lyrics: Nic - o - tine, val - ium, vi - co - dim, mari - ju - a - na, ec - sta - cy and al - cho - hol.

Nic - o - tine, val - ium, vi - co - dim, mari - ju - a - na,

ec - sta - cy and al - cho - hol. Nic - o - tine, val - ium,

vi - co - dim, mari - ju - a - na, ec - sta - cy and al - cho - hol. Oh.

Nic - o - tine, val - ium, vi - co - dim, mari - ju - a - na, ec - sta - cy and al - cho - hol.

vi - co - dim, mari - ju - a - na, ec - sta - cy and al - cho - hol.

P.M.

Nic - o - tine, val - ium, vi - co - dim, mari - ju - a - na, ec - sta - cy and al - cho - hol.

P.M.

Nic - o - tine, val - ium, vi - co - dim, mari - ju - a - na,

P.M.

N.C.   (D♭bass)

Co, co, co, co, co, co - caine._____ Yeah!

1/2

THE FIGHT SONG

WORDS & MUSIC BY BRIAN WARNER & JOHN LOWERY

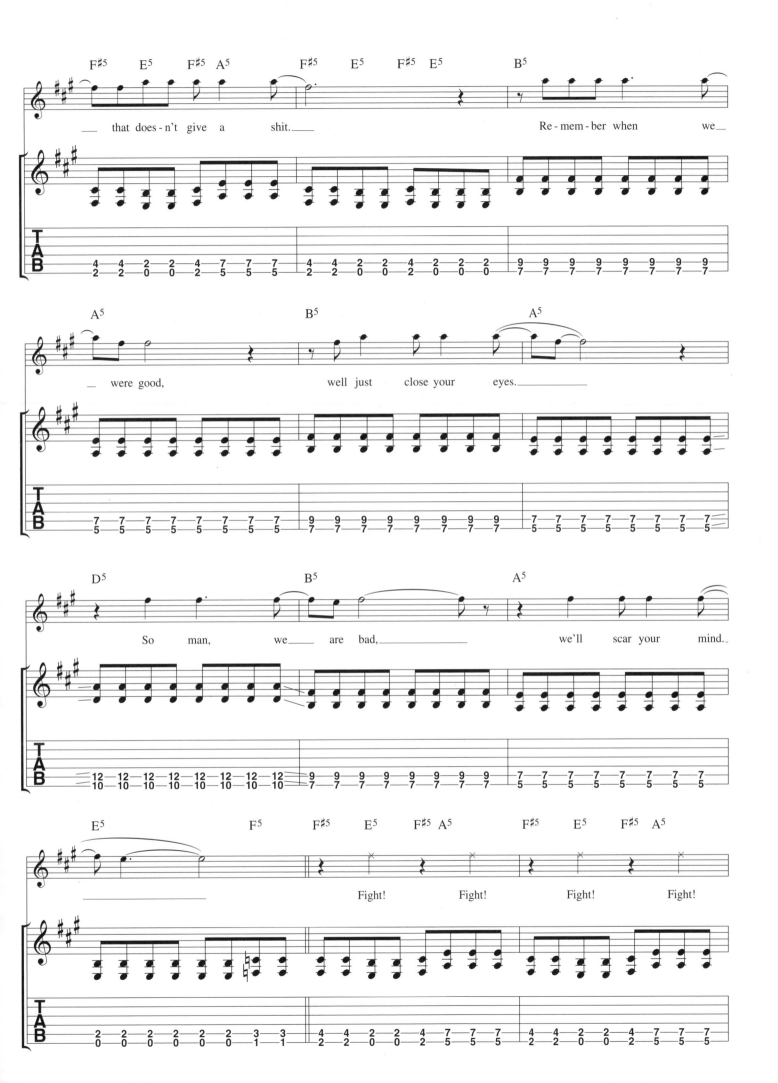

FLAVOR OF THE WEAK

WORDS & MUSIC BY STACY JONES

THE GREATEST VIEW

WORDS & MUSIC BY DANIEL JOHNS

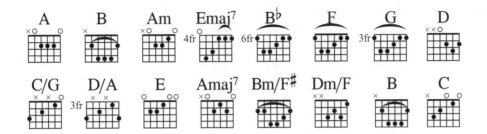

*Gtr. 2 plays octave higher

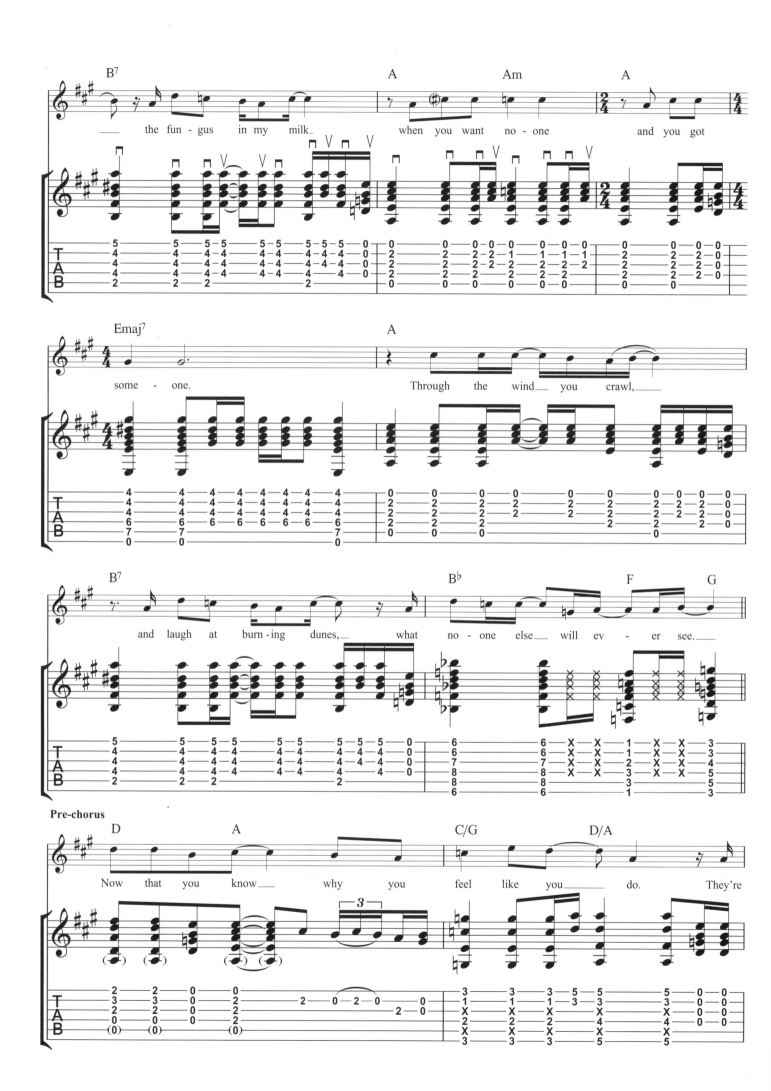

*play this composite part one octave higher if using 6 string guitar

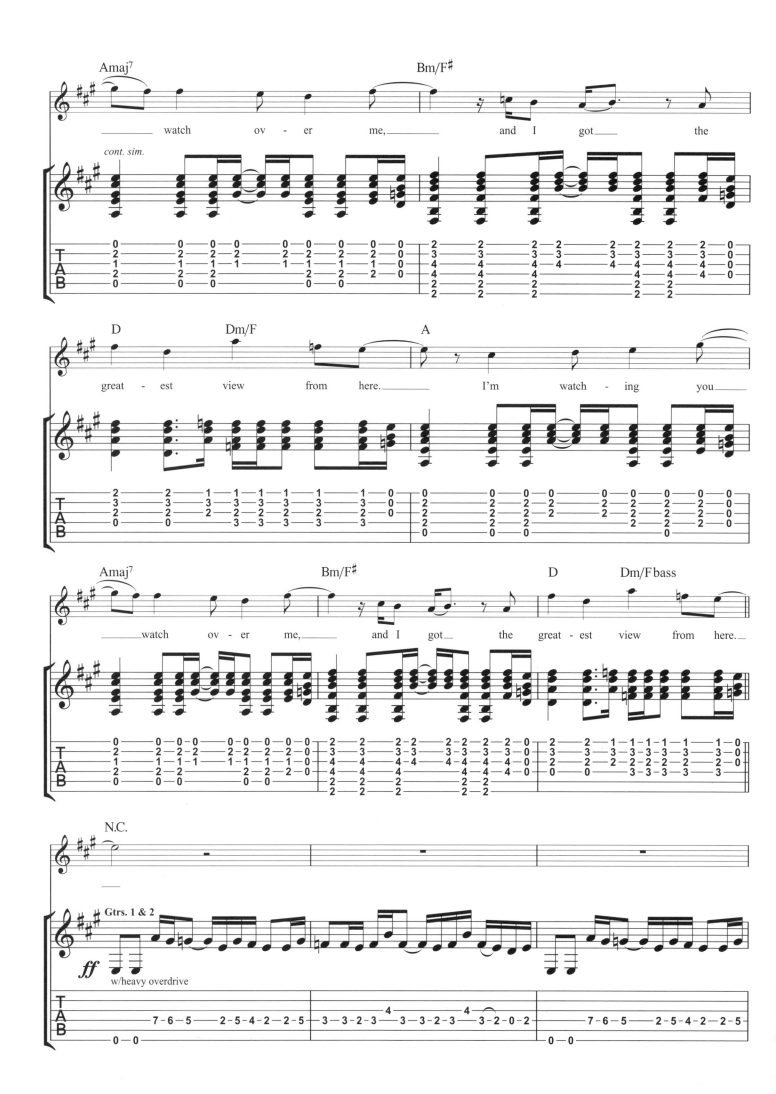

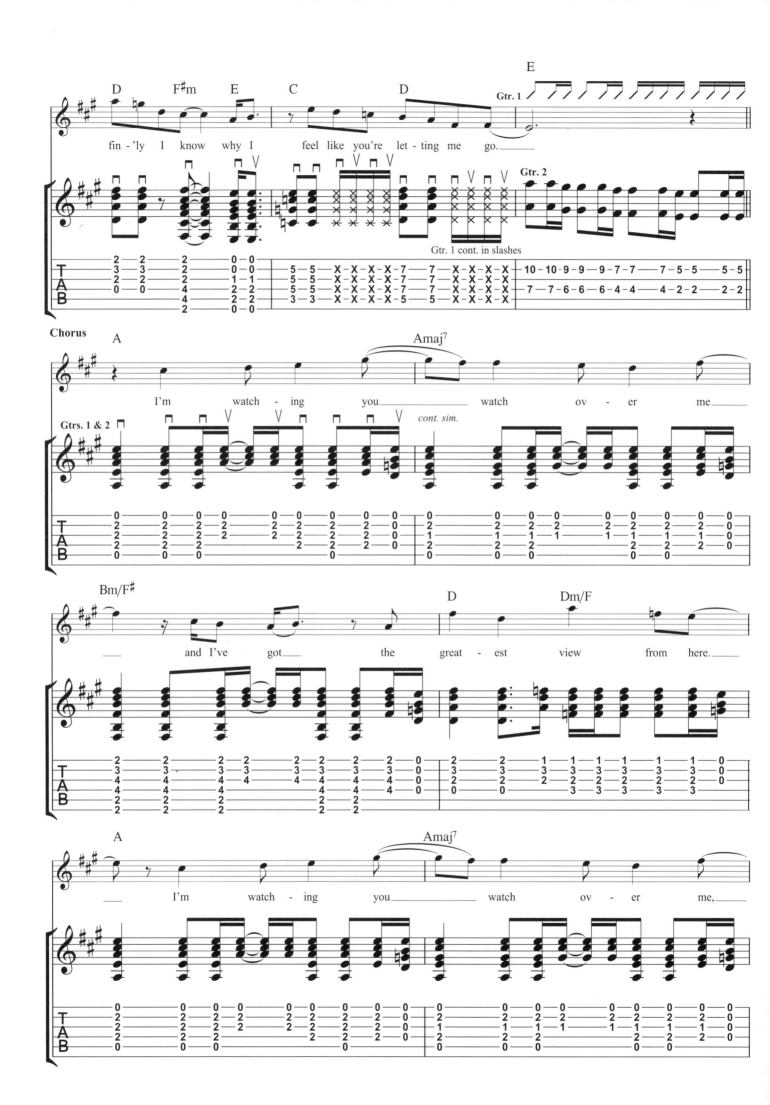

GIRL ALL THE BAD GUYS WANT

WORDS & MUSIC BY JARET REDDICK & BUTCH WALKER

tough guys, lis-ten-ing to rap met-al, turn ta-bles in her eyes, she likes them with a

mous-tache, race-track sea-son pass, driv-ing in a Trans - Am, does a mul-let

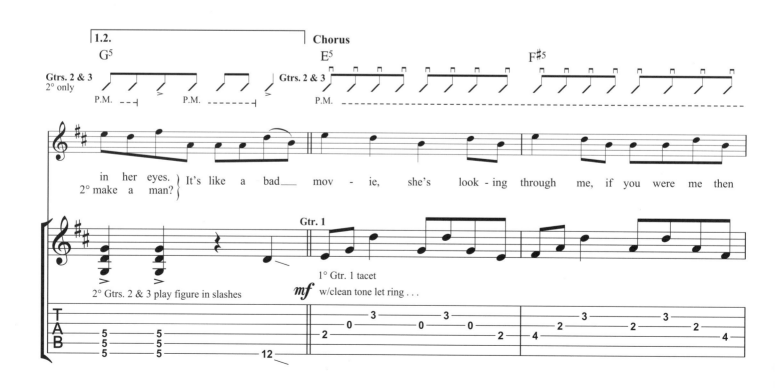

in her eyes. It's like a bad___ mov - ie, she's look-ing through me, if you were me then

2° make a man?

2° Gtrs. 2 & 3 play figure in slashes

1° Gtr. 1 tacet

mf w/clean tone let ring . . .

you'd   be   scream - in' "some - one shoot   me,"   as I   fail___ mis - 'rab - ly   try'n' to get the

girl   all   the   bad   guys   want.   'Cause she's the   girl   all the bad   guys

want.   want.   'Cause she's the

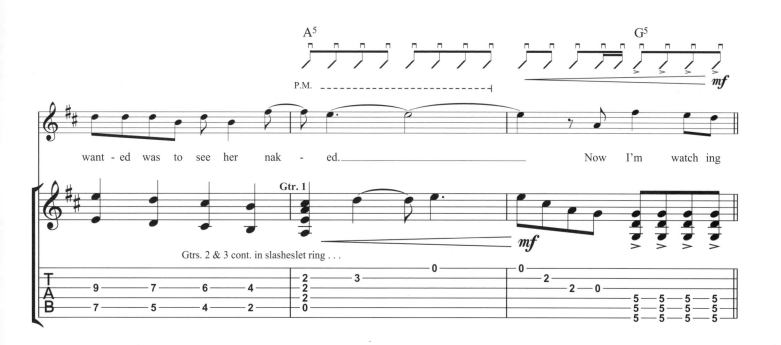

want - ed was to see her nak - ed._____ Now I'm watch ing

Pre-chorus

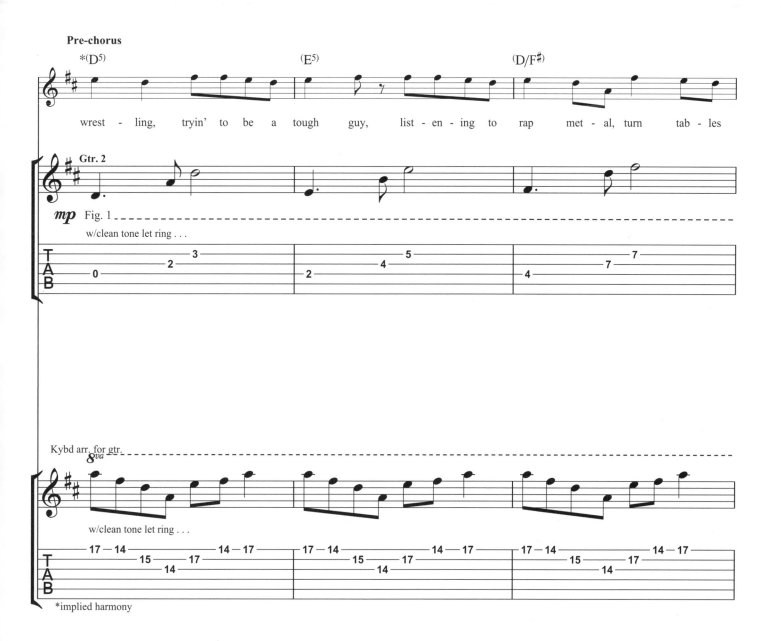

wrest - ling, tryin' to be a tough guy, list - en - ing to rap met - al, turn tab - les

*implied harmony

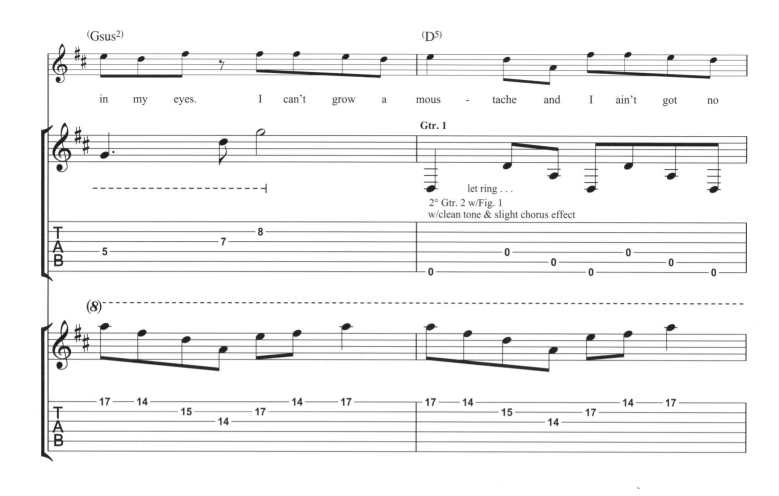

in my eyes. I can't grow a mous - tache and I ain't got no

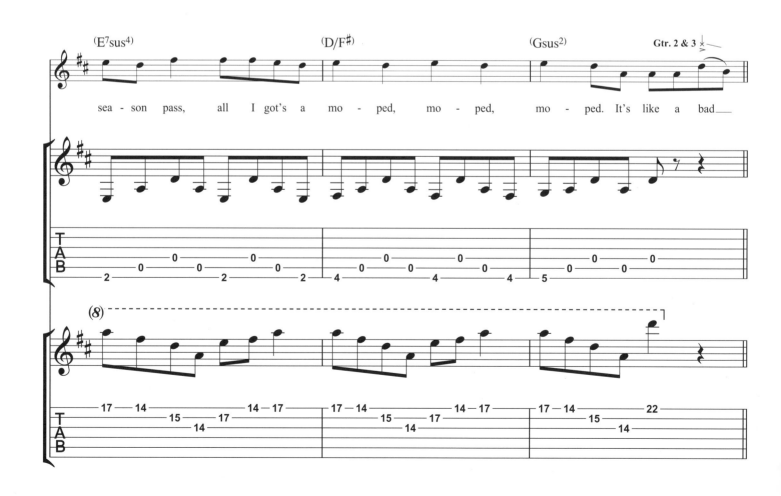

sea - son pass, all I got's a mo - ped, mo - ped, mo - ped. It's like a bad___

HERE TO STAY

WORDS & MUSIC BY JONATHAN DAVIS, JAMES SHAFFER, BRIAN WELCH, REGINALD ARVIZU & DAVID SILVERIA

All gtrs. are 7-string gtrs.
tuned down one whole step:

⑦ = A   ③ = F
⑥ = D   ② = A
⑤ = G   ① = D
④ = C

Moderately ♩ = 102

Intro:

N.C.

Band enters

1.2.   3.

Rhy. Fig. 1   end Rhy. Fig. 1

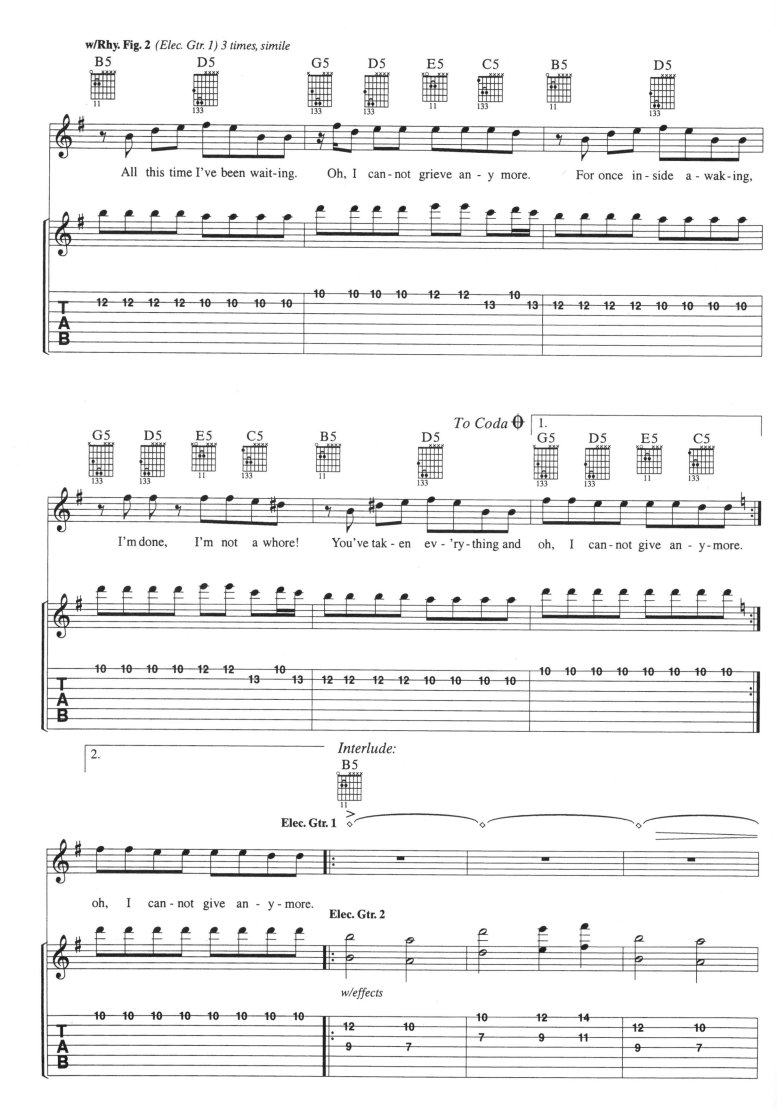

gon-na bring it down,___ gon-na break it down,___ gon-na bring it down,___ gon-na break it!

w/Rhy. Fig. 1 *(Elec. Gtr. 1)*
simile

N.C.   D.S. 𝄋 al Coda

Coda
**Elec.
Gtr. 1**

G5   D5   E5   C5

Cont. in notation

Oh, I can-not give an-y-more,

w/Lead Fig. 1 *(Elec. Gtr. 2) 4 times, simile*

N.C.

give an - y - more,

Elec. Gtr. 1

give an - y - more,

give an - y - more,   give an - y - more.

HIGHLY EVOLVED
WORDS & MUSIC BY CRAIG NICHOLLS

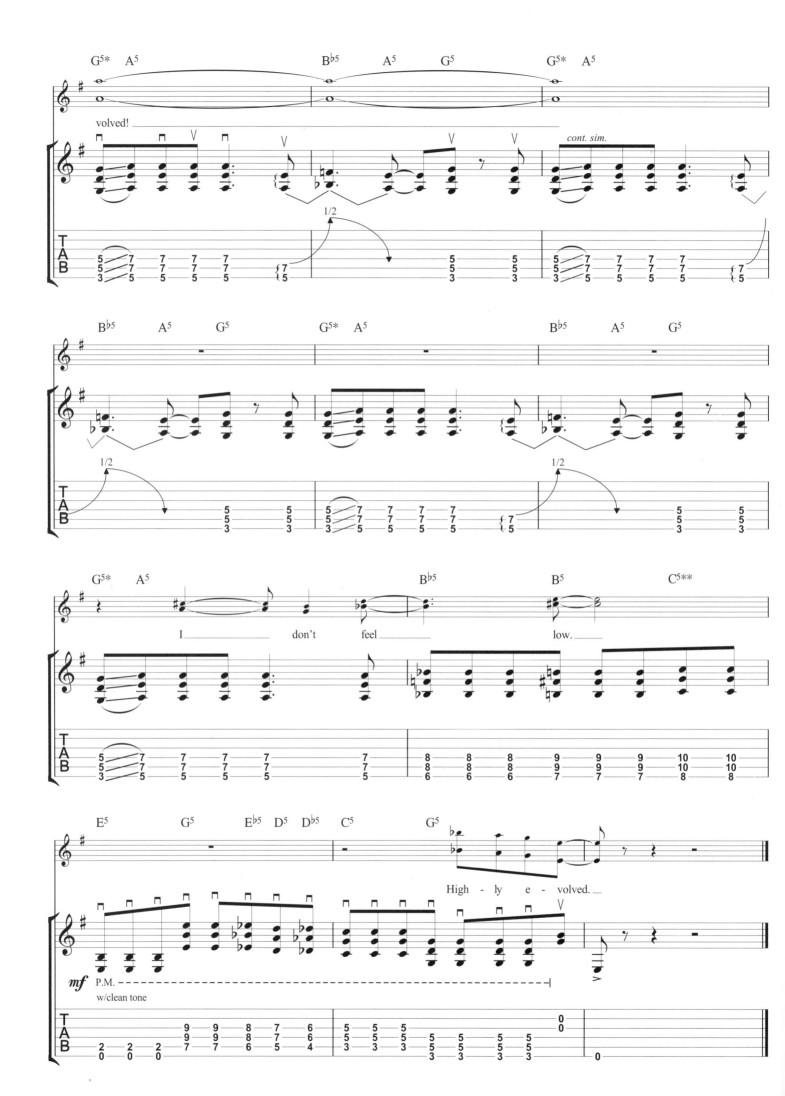

LAST RESORT

WORDS & MUSIC BY PAPA ROACH

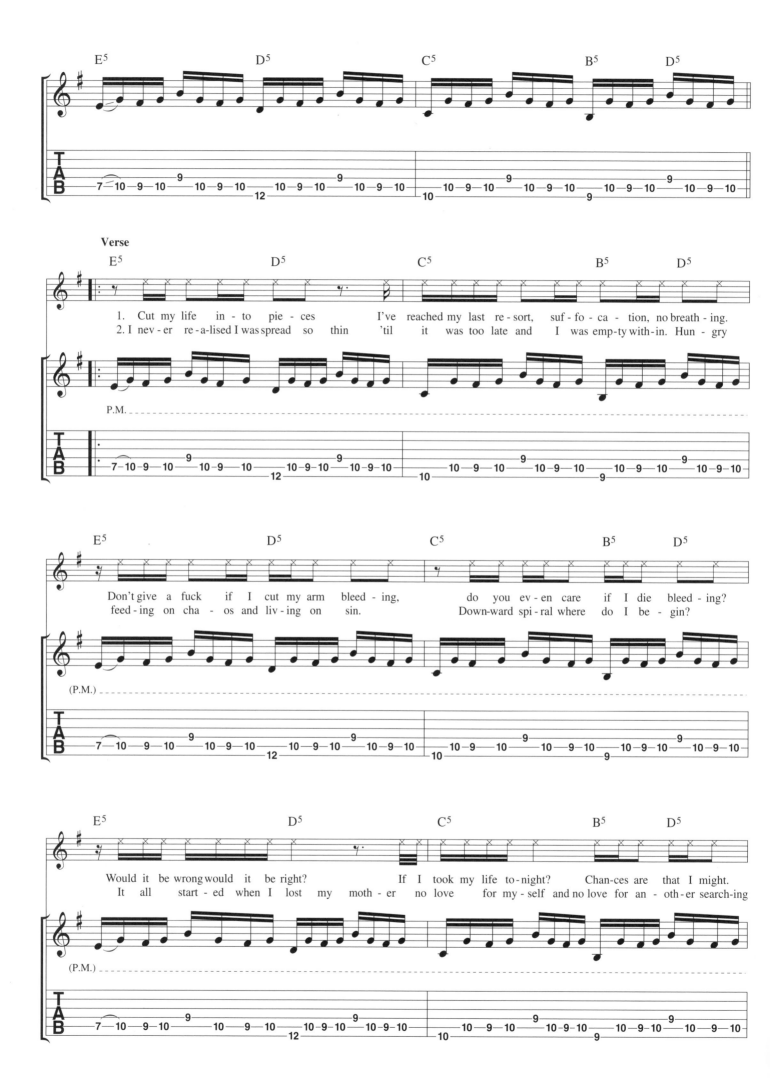

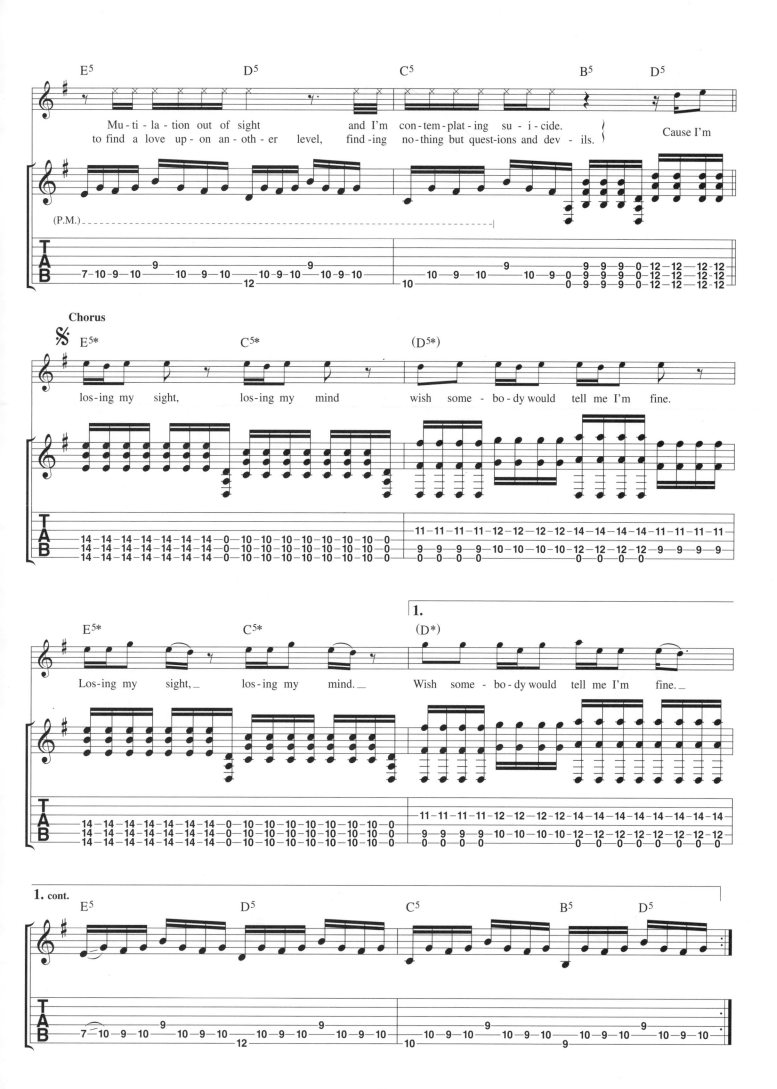

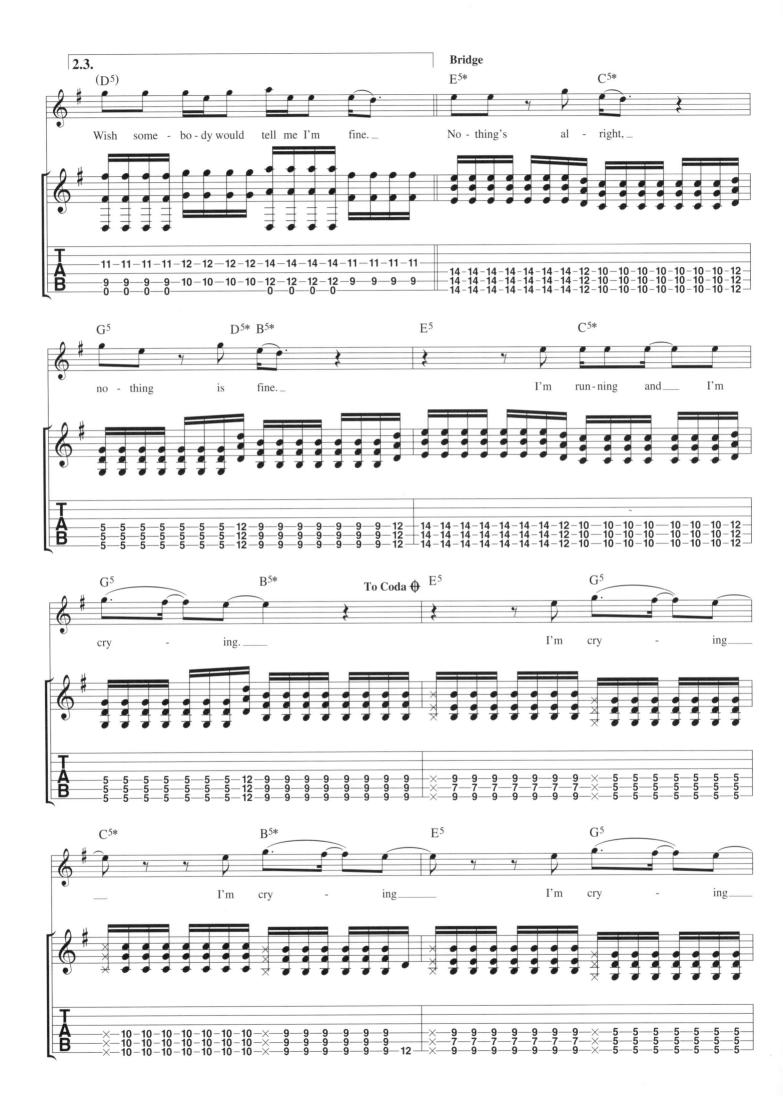

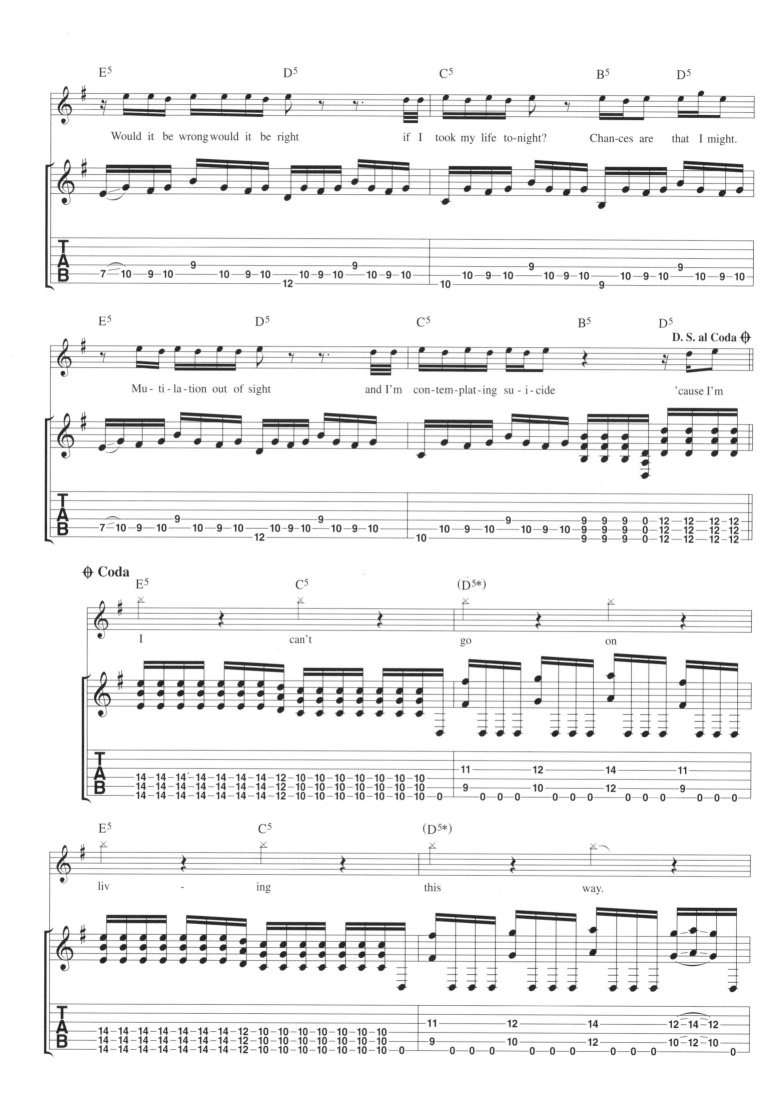

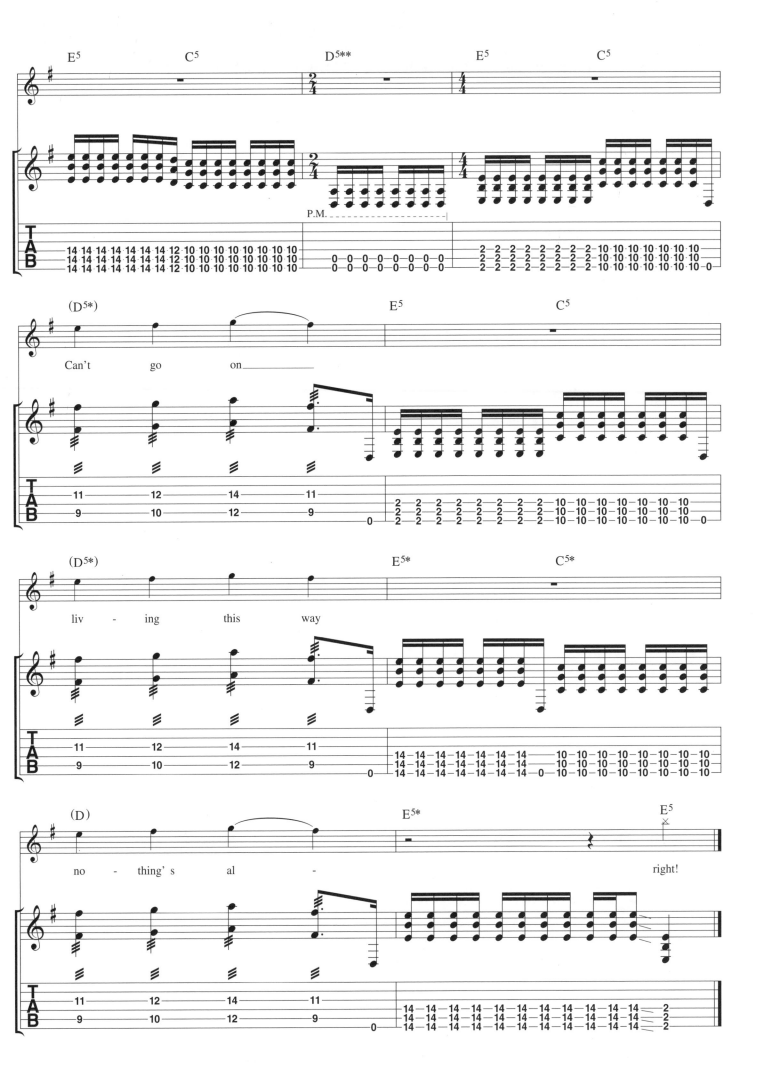

MOVIES

WORDS & MUSIC BY DRYDEN MITCHELL, TERENCE CORSO, TYE ZAMORA & MIKE COSGROVE

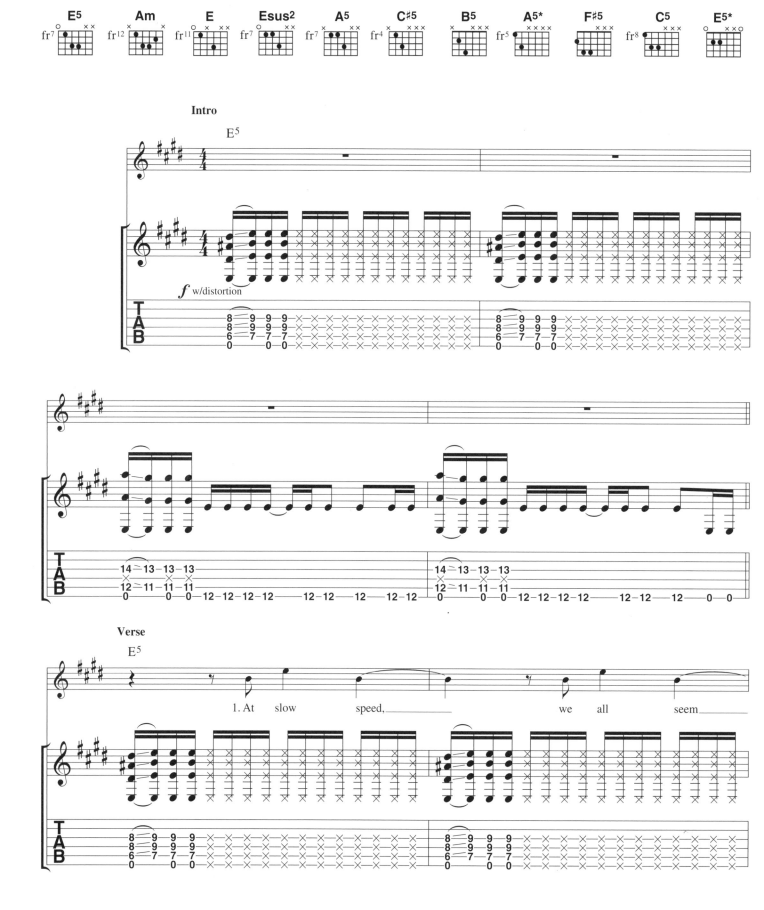

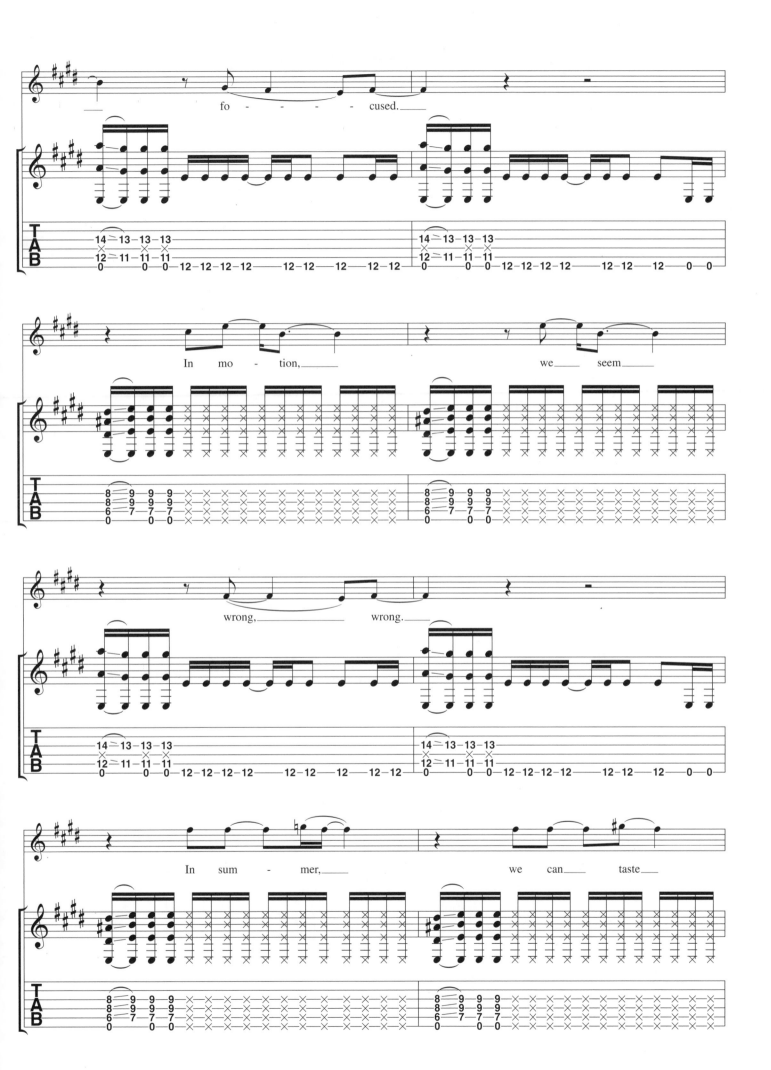

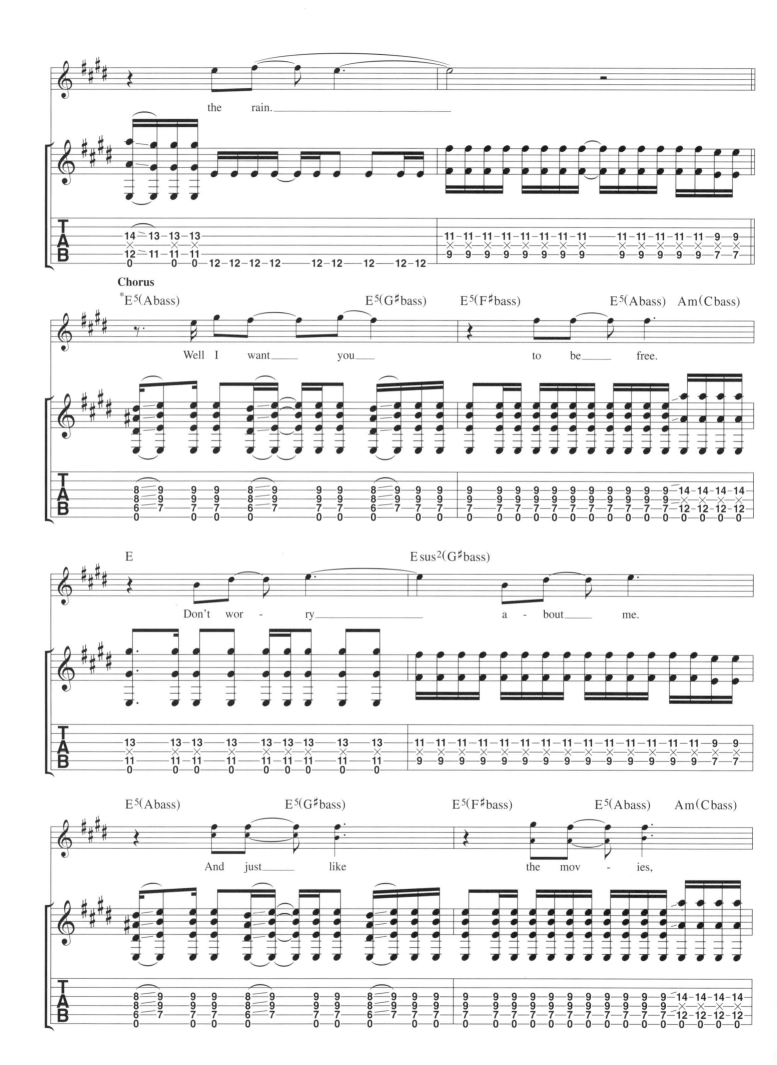

110

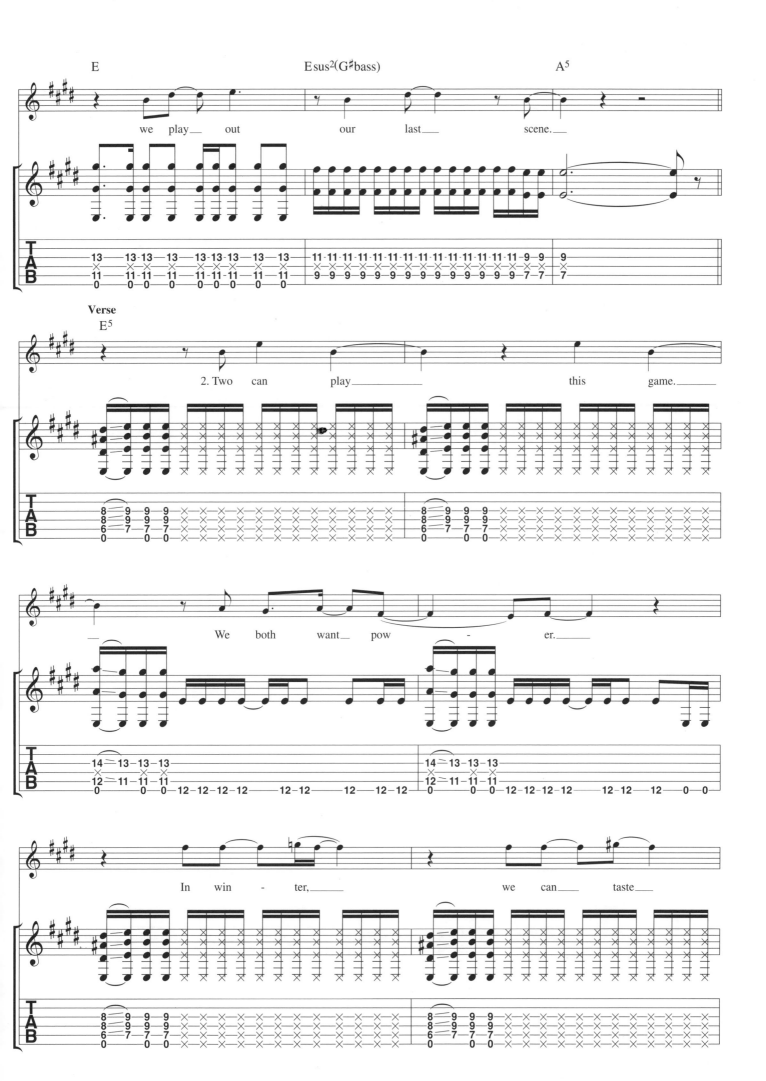

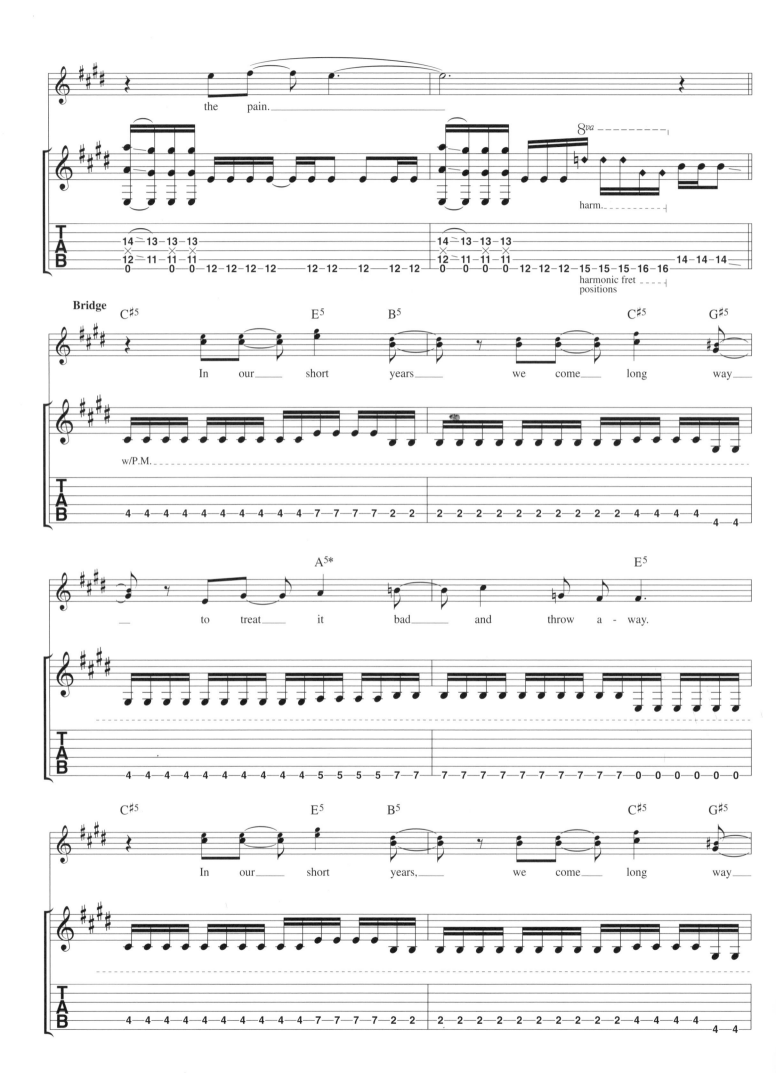

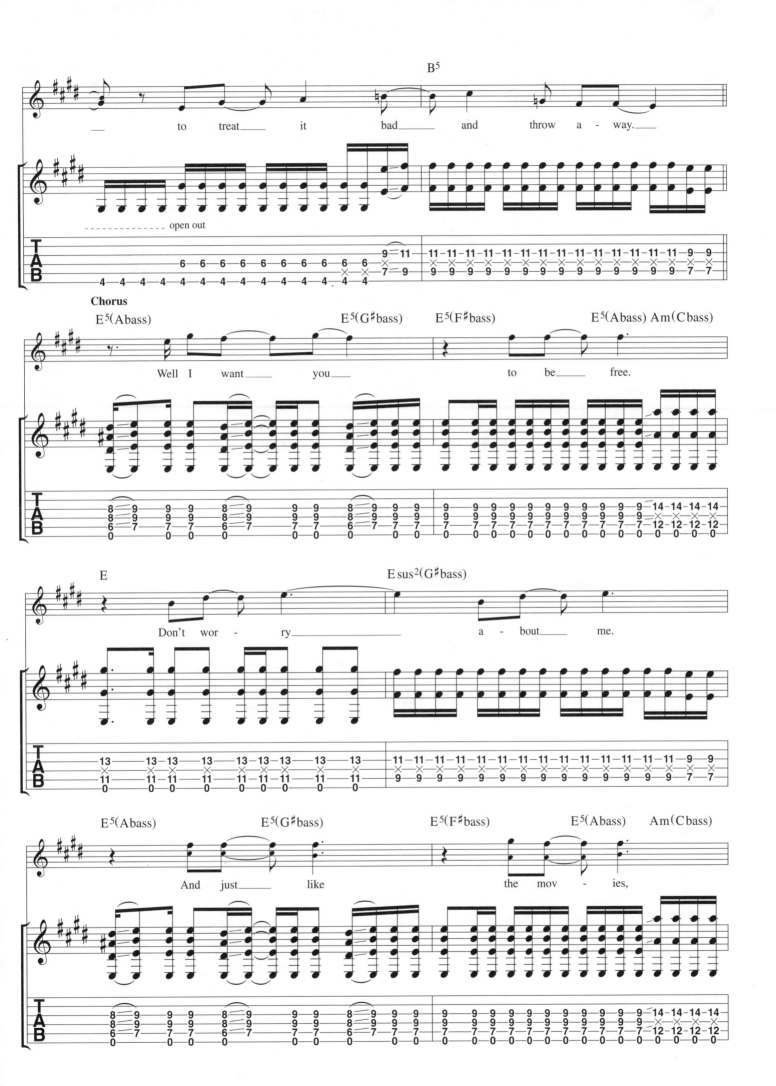

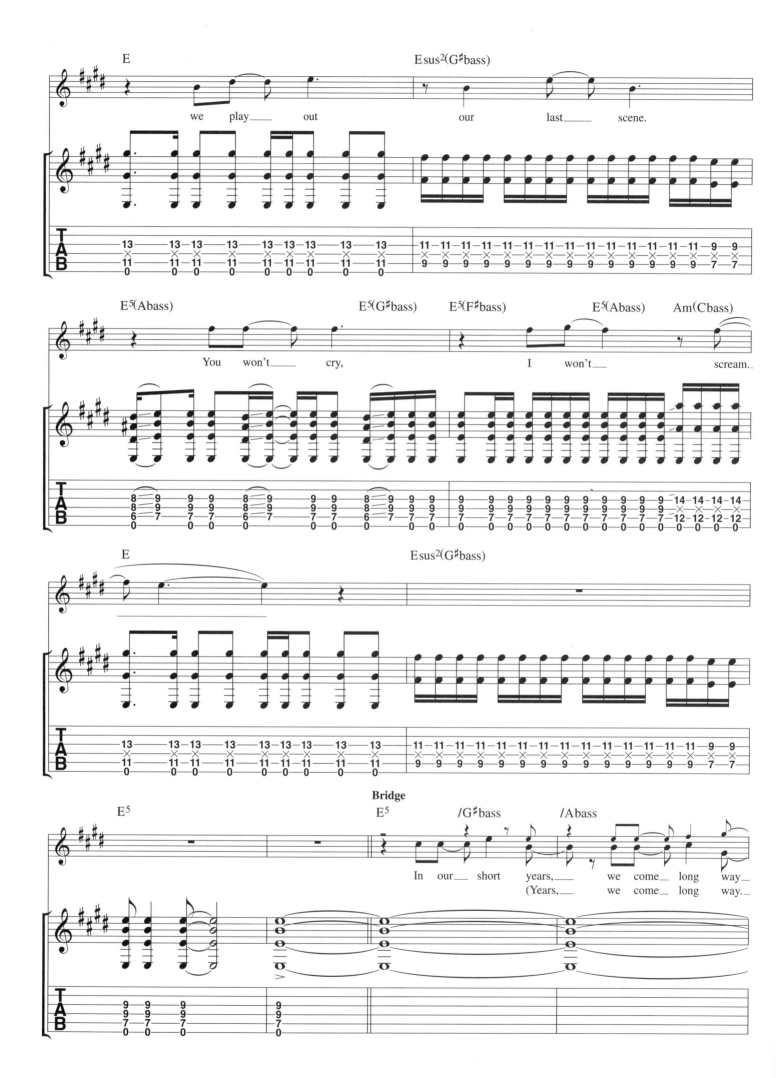

My Friends Over You

WORDS & MUSIC BY CYRUS BOLOOKI, CHAD GILBERT, JORDAN PUNDIK, IAN GRUSHKA & STEVE KLEIN

Drop D tuning
⑥ = D ③ = G
⑤ = A ② = B
④ = D ① = E

Intro ♩ = 180

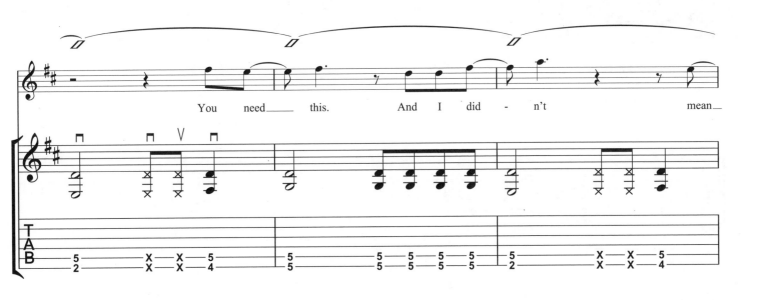

You need___ this. And I did - n't   mean___

_to   lead   you   on.___

D.S. al Coda
w/feedback

ff w/distortion

 CODA

Chorus

You   were   ev - 'ry - thing   I   want - ed___

Gtr. 1 w/Fig. 1 (*x4*)

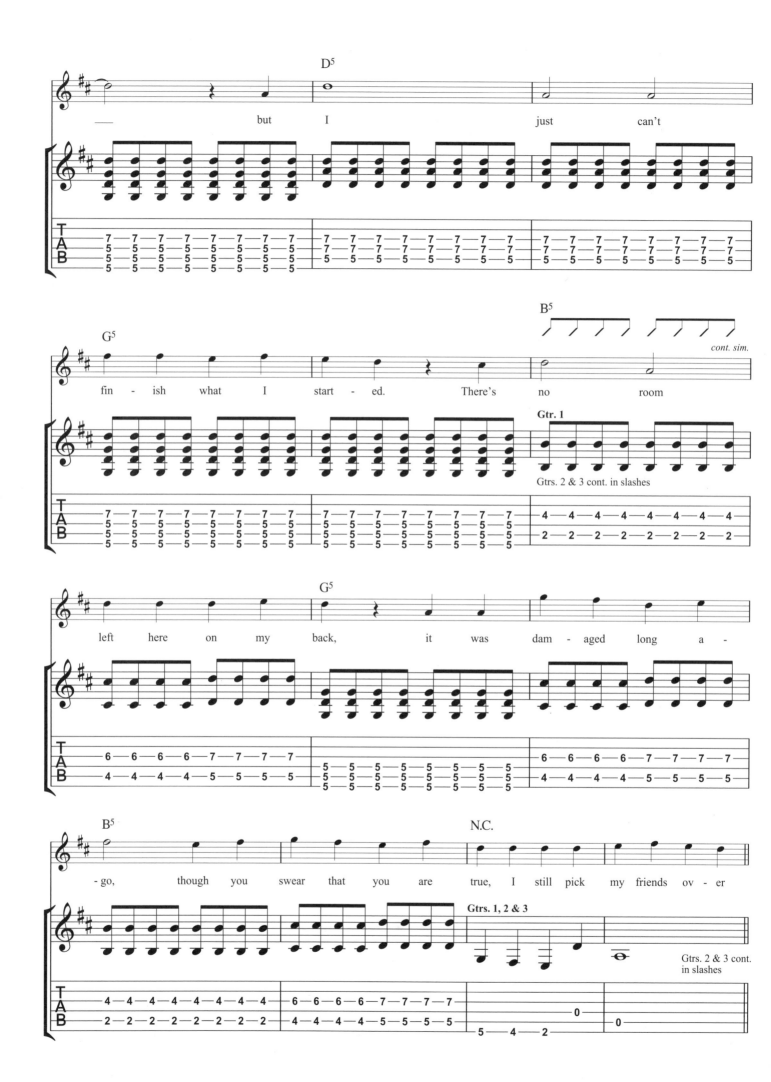

Outro

No One Knows

Words & Music by Josh Homme, Nick Oliveri & Mark Lanegan

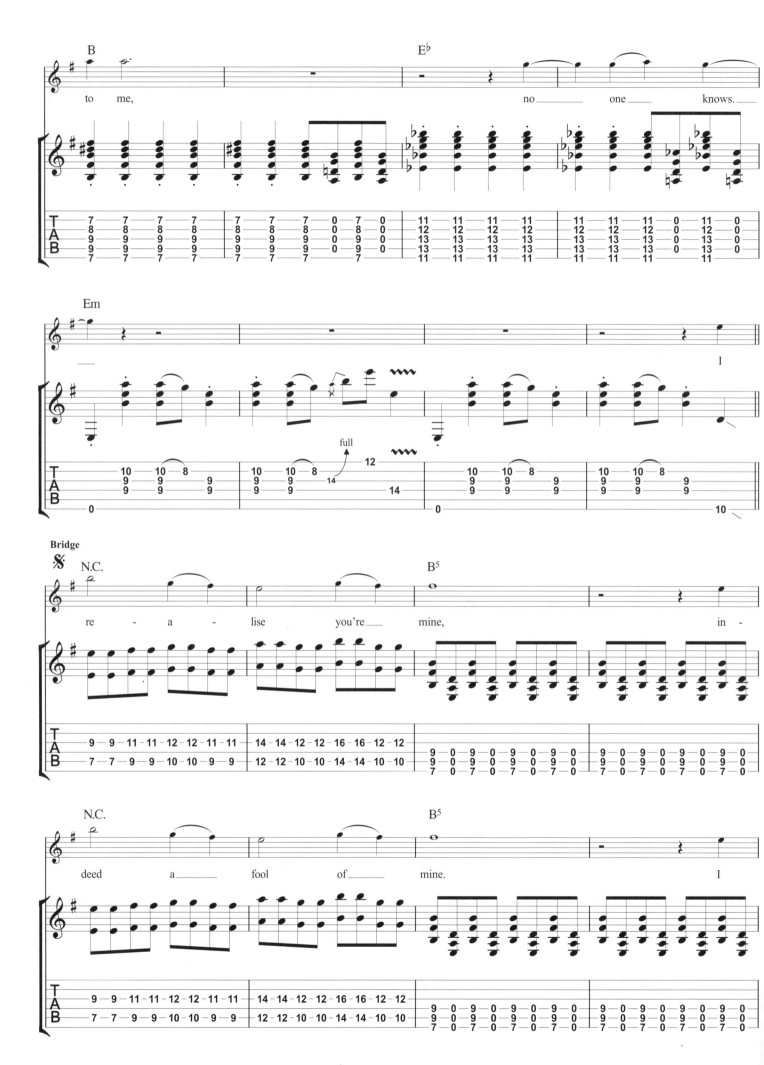

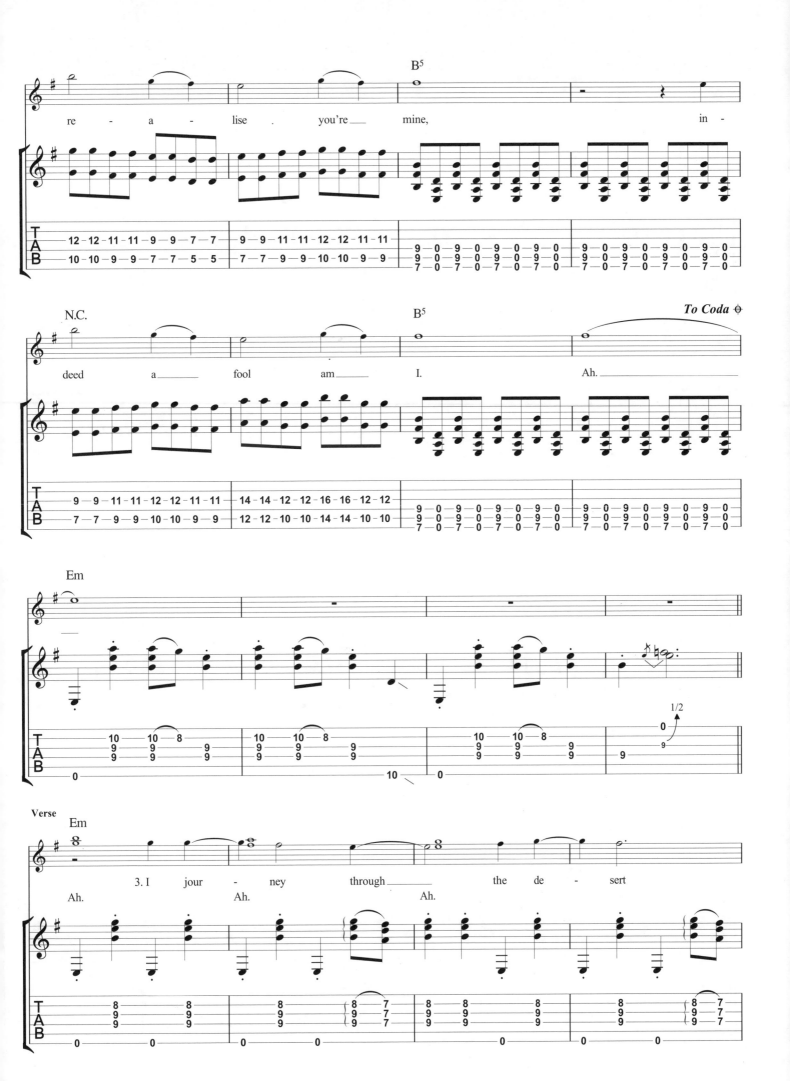

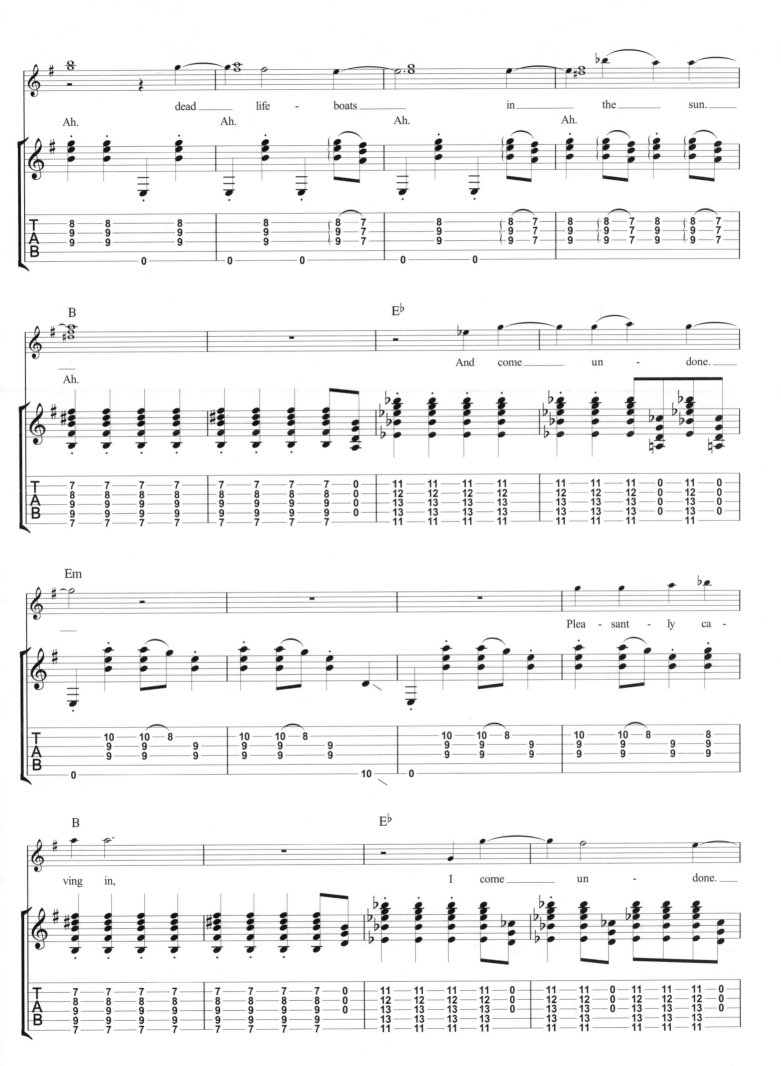

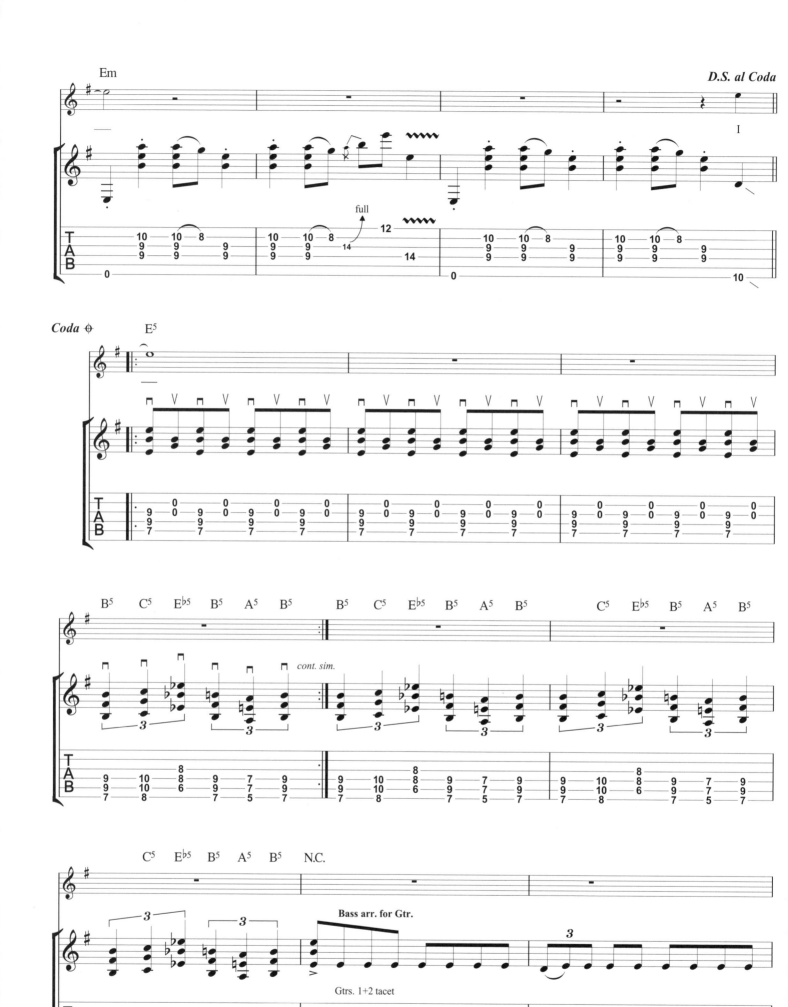

ONE STEP CLOSER

WORDS & MUSIC BY CHESTER BENNINGTON, ROB BOURDON, BRAD DELSON, JOSEPH HAHN & MIKE SHINODA

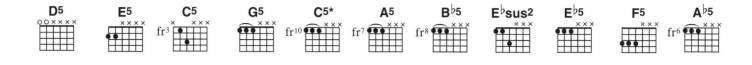

Tune gtr. Drop D tuning, down a semitone:

⑥ = C♯   ③ = F♯

⑤ = G♯   ② = A♯

④ = C♯   ① = D♯

139

PARTY HARD

WORDS & MUSIC BY ANDREW W. K.

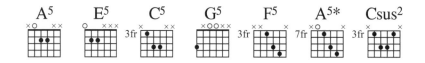

THE PEOPLE THAT WE LOVE

WORDS & MUSIC BY GAVIN ROSSDALE

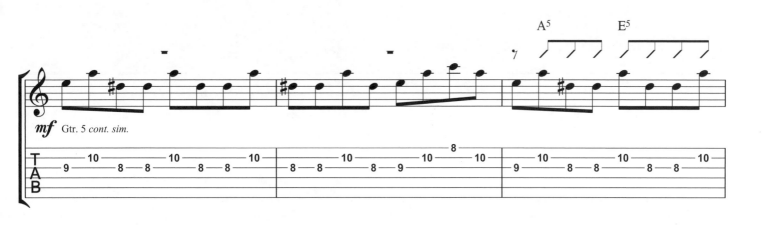

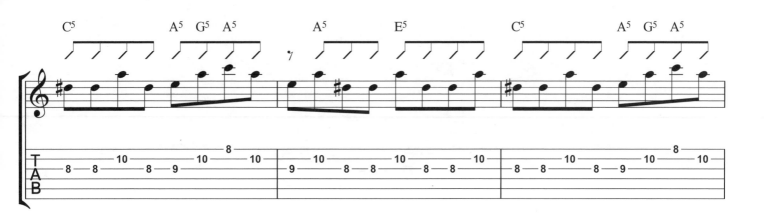

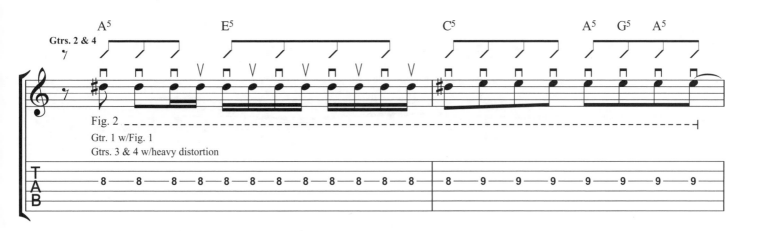

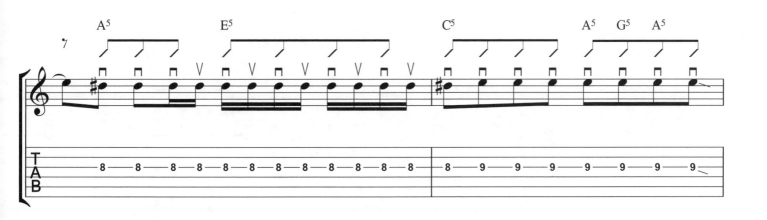

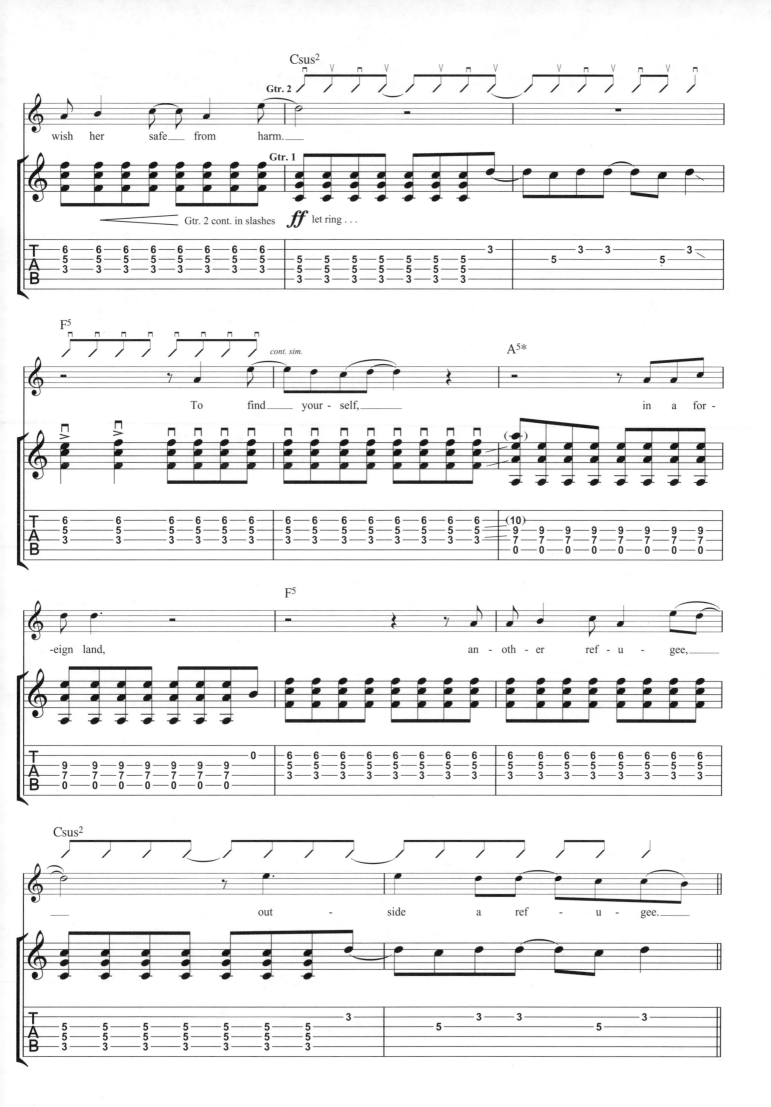

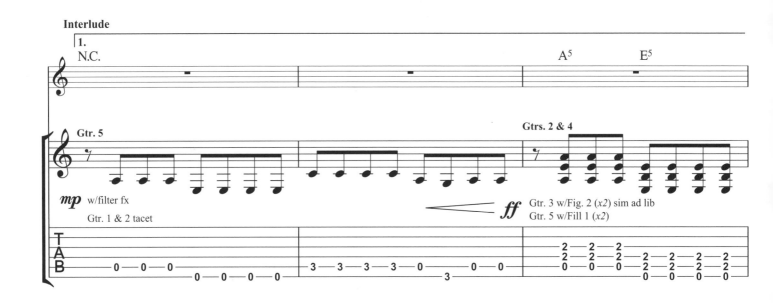

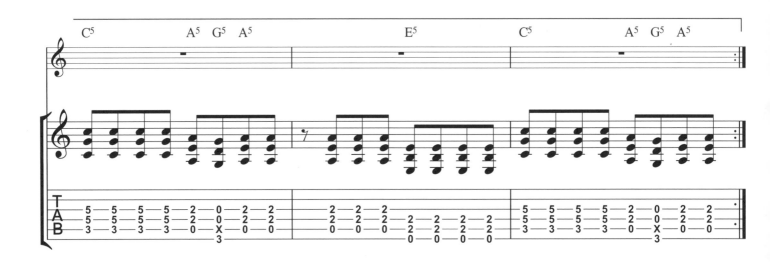

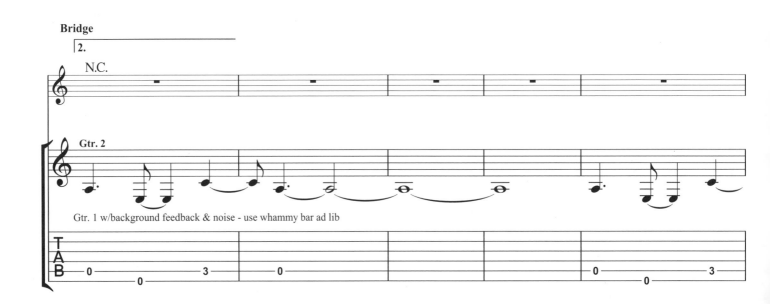

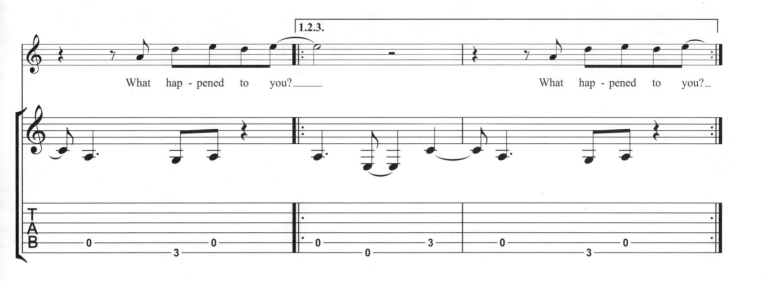

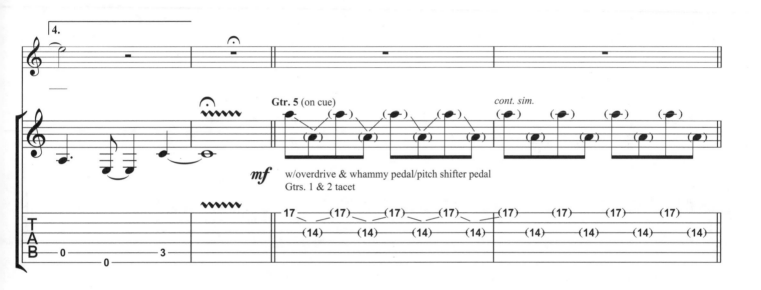

Instrumental

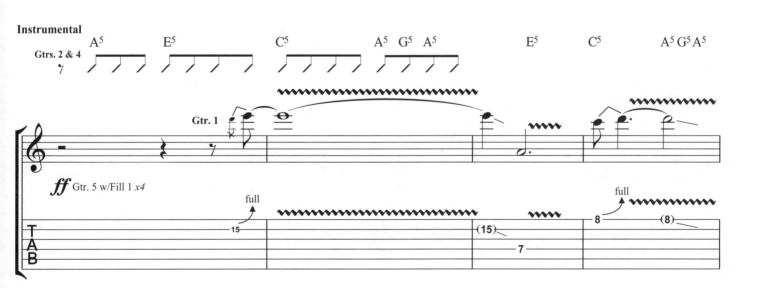

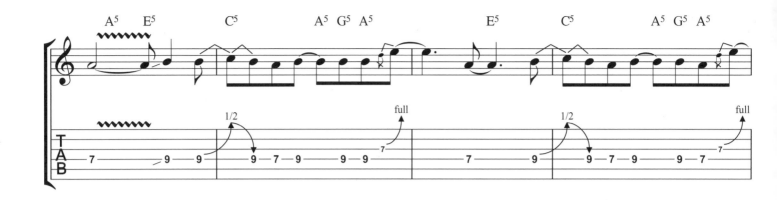

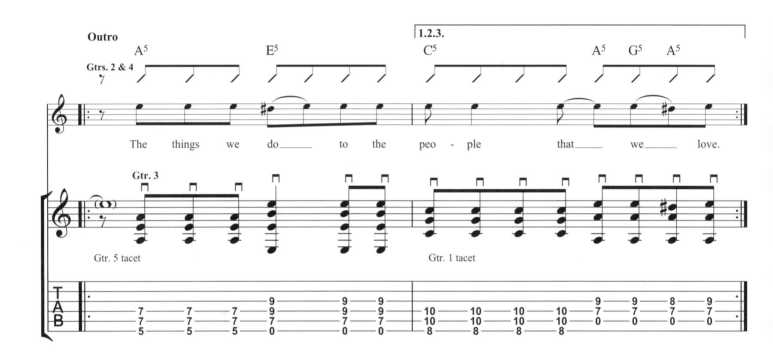

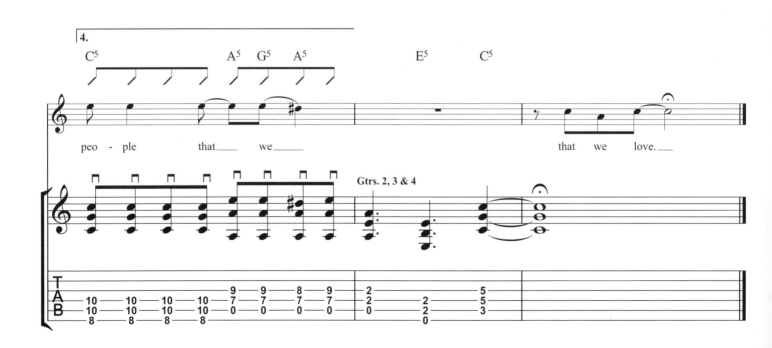

STACKED ACTORS

WORDS & MUSIC BY DAVE GROHL, TAYLOR HAWKINS & NATE MENDEL

⊕ *Coda 1*

Chorus

Gtrs. 1 & 2: w/ Riff A, 1st 4 meas., 1 1/2 times

N.C.

Stacked dead ac - tors, stacked __ to the raft - ers. Line __ up all the bas - tards all I

want is the truth. Stacked dead ac - tors, stacked __ to the raft - ers. Line __

__ up all the bas - tards and we cry when they all __ die blond. _____

Gtrs. 1 & 2 *8vb* - - - - - - - - - - - - - - - *loco* *8vb* - - - - - - - - - - - **Riff B** - - -

Harm. - -

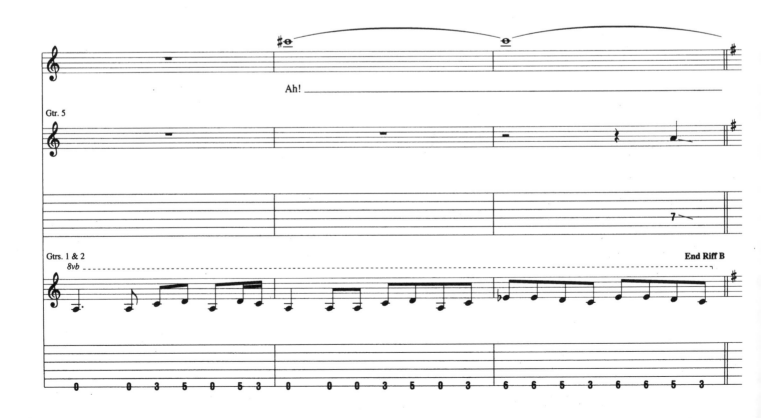

Ah! _____

Gtr. 5

Gtrs. 1 & 2 **End Riff B**
8vb -

160

D.S.S. al Coda 2

Hey, hey, ___

⊕ *Coda 2*

Gtrs. 1 & 2: w/ Riff A

N.C.

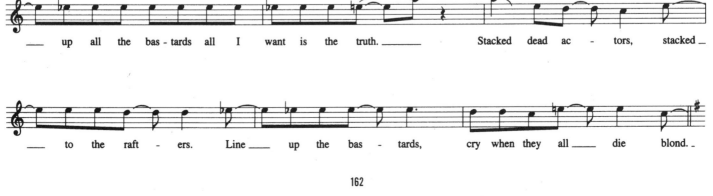

Stacked dead ac - tors, stacked ___ to the raft - ers. Line ___

___ up all the bas - tards all I want is the truth. ___ Stacked dead ac - tors, stacked ___

___ to the raft - ers. Line ___ up the bas - tards, cry when they all ___ die blond.

Outro

TRIBUTE

WORDS & MUSIC BY JACK BLACK & KYLE GASS

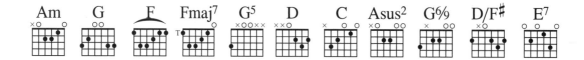

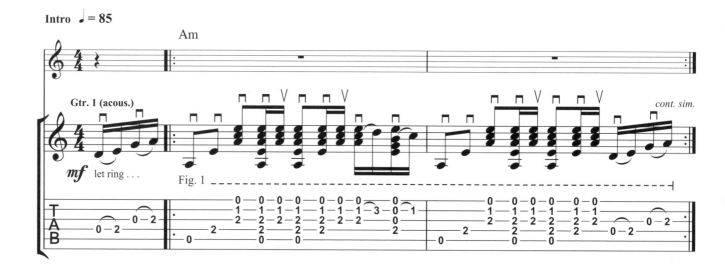

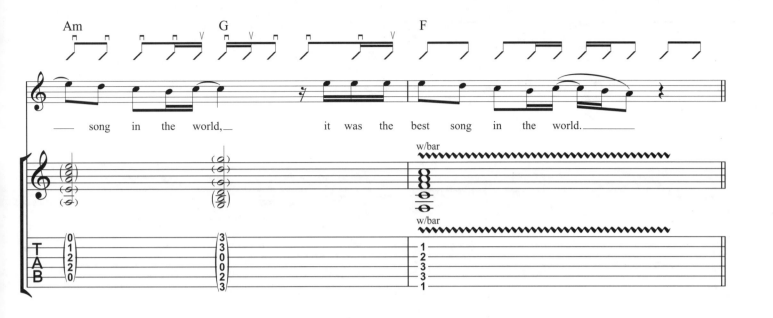

song in the world,___ it was the best song in the world._____

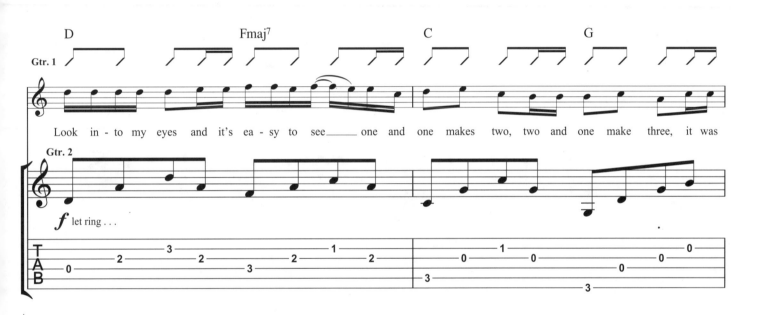

Look in - to my eyes and it's ea - sy to see___ one and one makes two, two and one make three, it was

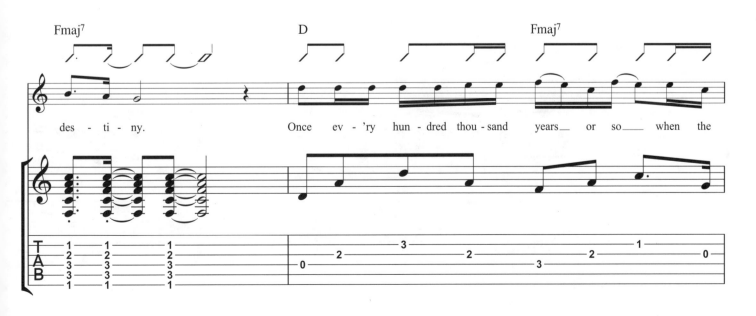

des - ti - ny. Once ev - 'ry hun - dred thou - sand years__ or so__ when the

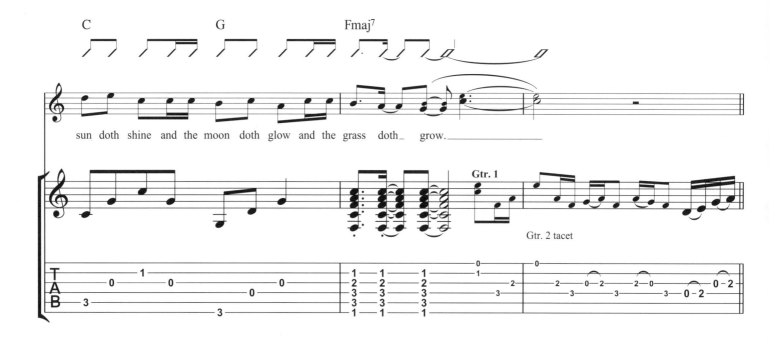

sun doth shine and the moon doth glow and the grass doth_ grow._____

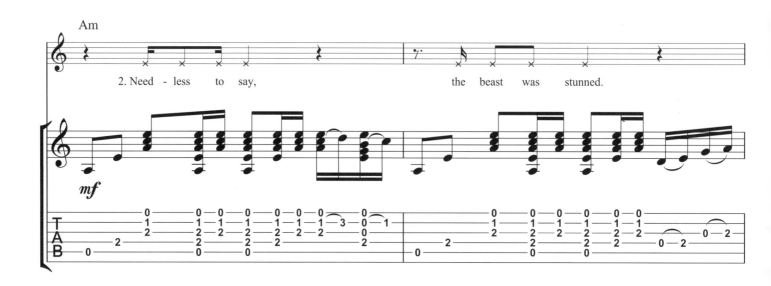

2. Need - less to say, the beast was stunned.

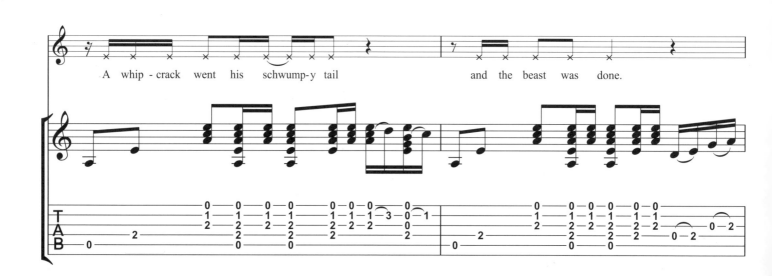

A whip - crack went his schwump-y tail and the beast was done.

He asked us,   "Be you an - gels?"

and we said,   "Nay.   We are but men." Rock!

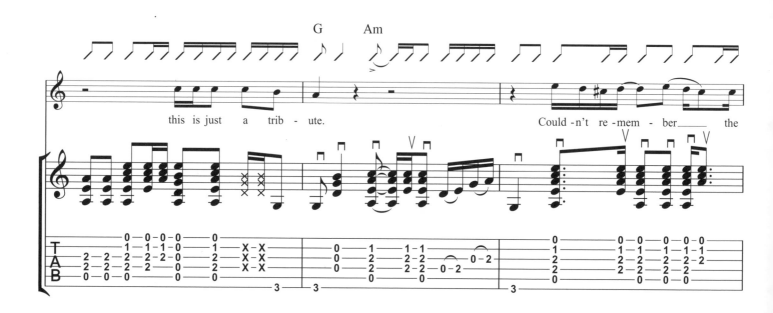

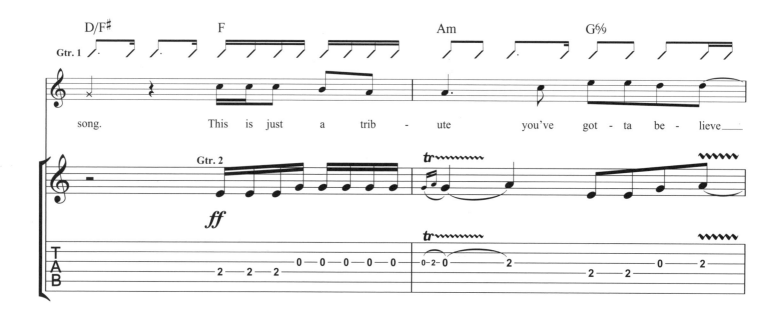

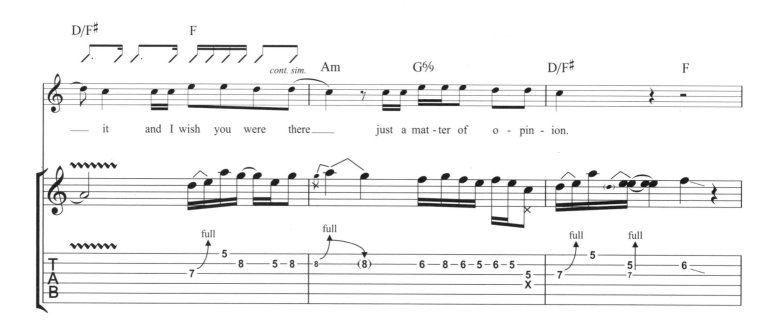

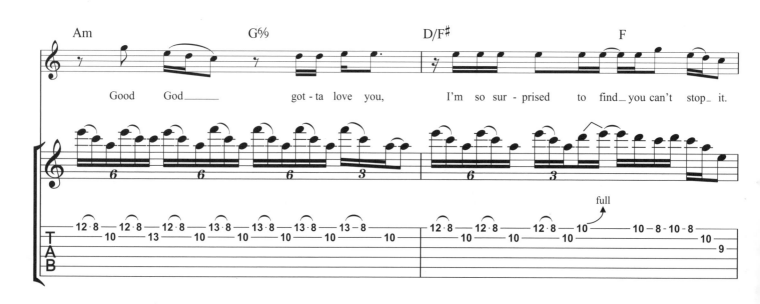

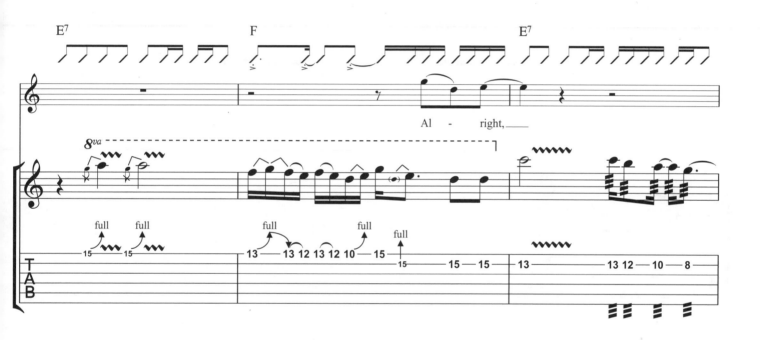

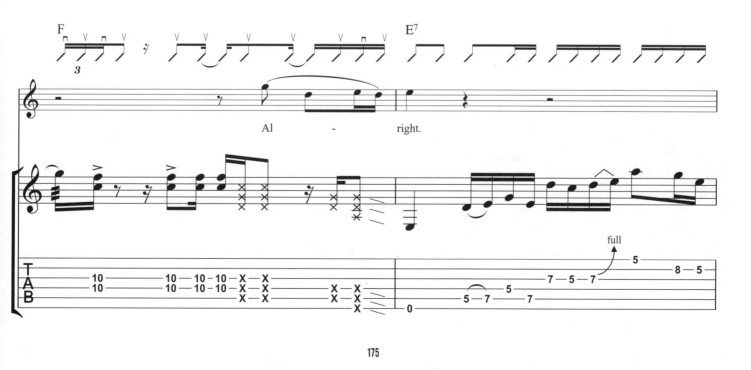

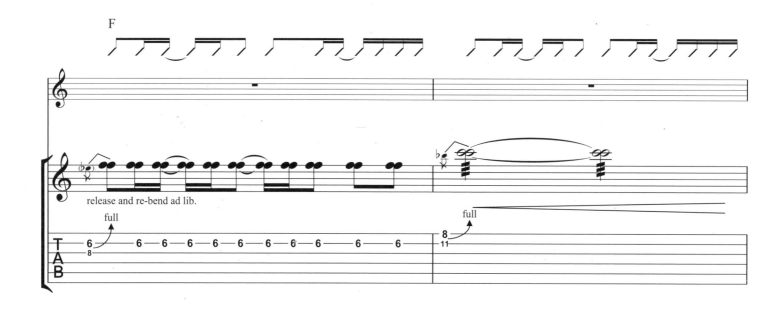

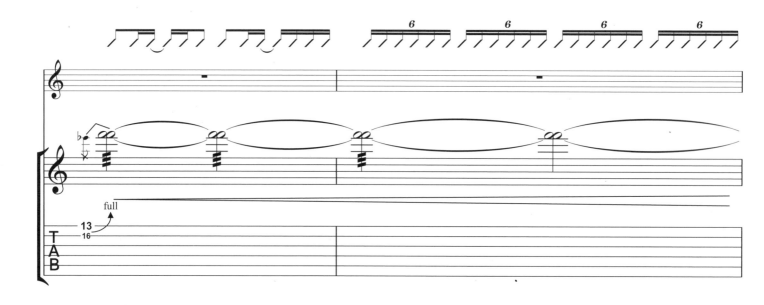

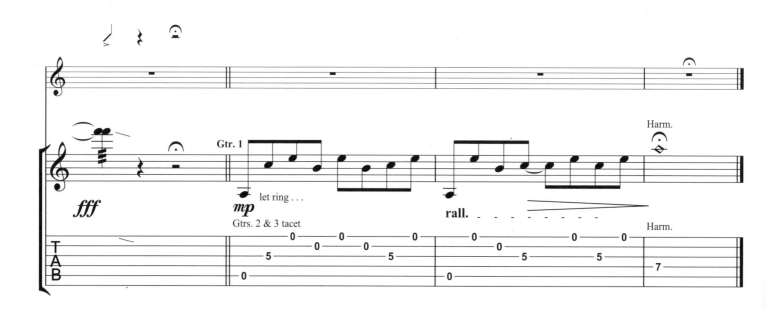